*The
Holloman
Story*

The Holloman Story

by
GEORGE F. MEETER

Eyewitness accounts of
Space Age research

The University of New Mexico Press 1967

CONTENTS

All illustrations are official United States Air Force photographs

*"Too low they build,
who build beneath the stars"*

—from "Night Thoughts"
by Edward Young (1683-1765)

ACKNOWLEDGMENTS

IT WILL BECOME OBVIOUS in reading this book that it could never have been written without the people who appear so prominently in its pages. To all these "makers and doers" of Holloman I feel deeply indebted for the wealth of detail above and beyond the news level which eventually permitted this fuller treatment of the Holloman story. The treatment—and any shortcomings—are my own; the heart of the matter rests in their personal accomplishments. Also to them and others gratitude is due for several different reasons. To single a few from the many is in itself an invidious proceeding, yet I feel that no acknowledgment here would be valid without mentioning, for instance, Lieutenant Colonel John McCurdy who made a Holloman writing job possible for me in the first place, Lieutenant Virgil Dominic, Master Sergeant George H. Mueller, and historian David Bushnell who were veritable answermen during our early years together in the Holloman information office, printing chief Joe S. Garcia for invaluable technical assistance many times over, staff engineer Orvie A. Steele who offered unlimited technical advice, artist Bill Leftwich who was as ready with personal encouragement. Very special thanks are due to Colonel John Paul Stapp, Major Eli Beeding, Lieutenant Colonel Fred Rohles, Major Herbert Reynolds, Lieutenant Colonel Leonard Sugerman, Mr. Arthur Abernathy, Mr. Fred Kuhn and several more who were kind enough to furnish bibliographical material related to these Holloman tales. Mr. Jake Kroehnke and Mrs. Ruth Mabe of the Army's White Sands Missile Range public information office supplied pictures and text concerning major activities at that end of the great missile range. Likewise many fine photo people at Holloman deserve appreciation not only for their creative excellence (some examples of which may be seen in this book) but for their downright personal enthusiasm and cooperation—among them Bill Gross and Hugh Ferguson who have ever been ready to improve the Holloman story with the Holloman picture. To these and others, the balloon crews, missile and drone crews, flight test crews, track test crews, maintenance crews, aeromedical and chimp-handling crews, guidance test crews—friendly people all who made the life of a Holloman writer both pleasanter and more fruitful with their endless funds of anecdote and information—it is my hope that these few words can be accepted as a true avowal of thanks. Also I would like to mention Time-Life correspondent Arch Napier of Albuquerque, New Mexico, who was good enough to read some of these pages in manuscript and introduce the subject with the necessary enthusiasm to the University of New Mexico's press director Roland Dickey—who in turn performed the things that led to the writing of this acknowledgment sheet.

And finally, to my wife Ricarda and daughters Markley and Joline for their cheerful never-failing applause, these thanks come as the pleasantest debt of all.

—GEORGE F. MEETER

The
Holloman
Story

1

PROLOGUE

The Space Age Comes to Holloman

ON THE SIXTEENTH OF JULY 1945 the first atomic bomb in history was exploded near Alamogordo, New Mexico. It was the first day of the Atomic Age. Just two years later a solitary missile streaked through the same gaudy blue skies from the Alamogordo Army Air Field. It was one of the first days of the Space Age.

The thin smoke plumes of that darting missile became the signal beckoning men, money, and more missiles until the empty desert wastes were empty no longer but crowded with all the evidences of both the Atomic Age and the Space Age. The little airfield grew into the sprawling complex of activities known as Holloman Air Force Base. It also grew as part of the Air Research and Development Command and then the Air Force Systems Command into one of the most unique applied research sites any nation could boast of, where many of the things that happen as well as the things designed and built to make them happen are so different they have never been duplicated anywhere else.

Truly fabulous things. Things of the Space Age.

At Holloman, Colonel John Paul Stapp rode a rocket sled 632 miles an hour and jolted to a water-braking stop in a second and a quarter, experiencing 40 times the pull of gravity and bursting tiny blood vessels in both eyes.

Lieutenant Colonel David Simons ascended 102,000 feet in a sealed balloon gondola—leaving behind him 99 per cent of the earth's atmosphere—and remained there 32 hours as the eyes and senses of a dozen eager scientists plying him with instructions from the ground below.

Captain Eli Beeding rode a sled on a shorter Holloman test track called the Daisy and in a split second of deceleration absorbed 83 times the weight of his own body—the greatest onslaught of G forces a man had ever taken and survived.

Captain Joe Kittinger was testing high-altitude survival equipment when he piloted an open balloon gondola almost 20 miles above the earth and stepped from there into the void—making the highest manned balloon flight, the longest free-fall, and the greatest parachute jump in all aerial history.

In another sealed gondola like that of Simons a young jet pilot, Cliff McClure, also sailed to the edge of space and almost baked there from a malfunction in the refrigerating system before his reluctant descent twelve hours after launch-off.

It was at Holloman that two chimpanzees, Ham and Enos, were transformed from chimps into "chimponauts" to make their world-famous trips through space from Cape Canaveral.

It was to Holloman that the Project Mercury human astronauts came for their indoctrination into the weird flying experience called weightlessness.

On the 35,000-foot captive missile test track, supersonic ball games have been played with live artillery shells and rocket sleds by catching the shell in the sled while both moved in tangential directions at velocities better than 1,000 miles an hour.

In a local swimming pool Holloman's "space frogmen" carried out an odd set of subgravity experiments extending all the way back to the theories of Archimedes.

On the Bopper crash-simulator scores of aeromedical volunteers have been treated like pellets in a giant sling-shot as the mechanism built up its G forces and abrupt stops to find out what happens to space travelers under reentry conditions.

To plot how a missile goes from here to there the miracle of inertial guidance is studied in the most elaborate test complex ever constructed for wringing out the secrets of every Air Force missile that flies.

There is also a stratosphere chamber like few in the world, where space flight is simulated through a gamut of variant stresses including plus and minus temperatures, humidity, vibration, infrared radiation—in short everything in space but weightlessness.

And there are other things, just as fabulous. Like science fiction which has outstripped fiction itself.

To find Holloman you only have to reach Alamogordo in the south-central part of New Mexico and then drive along Highway 70 to a point ten miles west of that thriving "Spaceport" city. There you'll find a huge blue-and-white sign topped by a sleekly shaped missile pointing in from the road to make it clear that the gate ahead leads to one of the Air Force's true Space Age outposts.

When the first A-bomb exploded and this was only a bombing range its people were very few. Now they number in the thousands.

Most are people of science and technology working endlessly at the task of probing the future. Among them are engineers, mathematicians, astronomers, physicists; doctors, chemists, physiologists, psychologists; experts in ballistics, aeronautics, electronics, aerodynamics; ex-wartime flyers, supersonic test pilots, one-time German and American antagonists now German-American science teams; rocket designers, balloon launchers, radar technicians, computer specialists; inventors, dreamers, thinkers, doers; stargazers and moon-watchers . . . men watching the future, gazing into space, working multitudinous kinds of wizardry to launch man into space.

Everywhere they are to be found in their offices, laboratories, blueprint cubicles, on the flight line, in the air, in and around test chambers, at instrument panels, in computer rooms—planning, devising, accomplishing countless tasks involving missiles, tracking systems, electronic systems, weapon systems, space capsules, men, equipment, and ideas.

Here the ideas of tomorrow are bruited about today.

Working from drawing board to firing range they help perfect the latest interceptors, bombers, decoys, diversionary systems. With the most astounding devices they delve into the problems and hazards of space travel. Ever since that first missile they have been slowly accumulating solid hardcore knowledge (and then faster and faster, like everything in the Space Age) in fields like space medicine, space biology, physics, optics, orbital mechanics, cosmic ray research, acceleration and reentry research, satellite tracking, missile tracking, rocket propulsion—any number of areas related to man's latest and greatest dream, that of traveling to and returning from the great out-there.

Whole bevies of deadly birds have been hatched from their electronic nests and made to fly, such as the Genie, Rascal, Matador, Mace, X-7, Sidewinder, Falcon, the "GAM" series. A dozen high-performance fighter weapon systems have been "married" for operational compatibility. Aerial target drones ranging from the subsonic to the supersonic have been developed in countless hot runs. Supersonic sled testing has reached the Mach 5 of hypersonic. The state-of-the-art in inertial guidance testing has exceeded the magnitude of the systems tested. Celestial guidance testing has begun reaching out toward the stellar spaces.

In short, here at Holloman where the San Andres and Sacramento mountains and scraggly brown desert completely encircle these lonely people, the challenge of the future is being met in so many ways that it might be said space itself has become the ideal and beckoning dimension.

All this may sound as if it were "space" beckoning the present writer when he arrived at Holloman early in 1958 after seven years of traveling over Europe as a civilian with the Air Force. But that would be too glamorous a statement. Actually to such a newcomer the matters just referred to could hardly even have been suspected, much less known through the vague comments enroute concerning "that place where they launch the missiles."

And thus coming as a writer to undertake the Holloman part of the Air Force story was even more bewildering—as confusing as the thought of it was exciting and attractive.

How little one had heard in Europe about missiles! True, there were news items, a few feature articles about Redstones, Thors, Jupiters, ICBM flights, as if that was all that could be said. But here at the scene itself—at the firing pads, the flight lines, the test stands, the blockhouses full of technicians swarming everywhere under the stress and tension of countdowns—how swiftly different!

Here where everyone from high-altitude task scientist to cafeteria snack server was already and obviously missile conscious. Here where the gossip was more likely to be about balloon launches, rocket sleds, upper air research rockets, booster thrust, sonic booms, supersonic test tracks, liquid propellants, ramjets and turbojets, lunar probes, solar furnaces, Falcons, Aerobees, Firebees, ballistic missile sites, space capsules, satellites, nose cones, zero-gravity—the heterogeneous litter of fascinating and mystifying matters of the Space Age itself.

What person at Holloman—technician or typist, mathematician or mechanic, research engineer or reorder clerk—hadn't heard of John Paul Stapp, Joe Kittinger, the Manhigh balloons, the Aerobee-Hi, the space chimps, the activities on the missile range which shimmered off whitely in the distance?

And what newcomer wouldn't be drawn into it likewise?

For they were all conscious of such things. And it was one of the first curious facts to strike a newcomer; not only was this Atomic Age and Space Age a strange and fascinating new world but the people involved in it were aware of being involved in the greatest thrill of any age, a thrill even against its grimmer foreshadowings that might be equated with the destruction of all mankind.

They were like people moving to the very quick of life. Like the people of London during the Blitz, subtly engaged at the summit of their careers, so preoccupied with living that death itself was the abstraction.

For death also lurked around the corner at Holloman. Though it was rare even to have an injury to be reported. And both cause and effect could be seen at once in all the precautions and safety rules, the air police cordons, roadblocks, fire trucks, ambulances, range safety officers, destruct systems to control the flights of missiles, blockhouses for the countdown crews, loudspeakers everywhere for the warning of the individual against X-times or T-times, all these and more as only too familiar adjuncts to every mission, every project, every activity going on at this "place where the missiles were launched."

The hazards of life were being challenged by the quick of life.

And how quickly the newcomer was made a part of it. Attending commanders' briefings, reading technical reports, devouring "space" books, studying project films, visiting test sites, going on missions, chatting with task scientists, engineers, technicians, taking notes, notes, notes. And hurrying back to a desk in a cluttered corner to write about it.

For a while the ignorance was so enormous it was like not knowing which end of a missile is up. But gradually that passed. And gradually the story came clear. Of an effort called "research and development" as the very focal point of this nation's most penetrating look into tomorrow. Of efforts that had banded men together in these lonely stretches of the desert, at this outpost called Holloman. Men of talent, some with genius, above all "men of good will" submitting themselves, their lives, their thoughts and most soaring hopes to every imaginable test and stress on the way to a no longer earthbound future. Like other far-spread sites with other such men the Holloman complex has been and remains a truly unique one. Many of its missions, experiments, test projects have neither origin nor continuance except here. Some have become prominent on a national scale; others have been carried out on the plodding ground of applied research, only in very quiet ways enlarging the subtler concepts of man. All together they may have added a cubit to man's intellectual stature—simply by bringing him closer to the stars.

No one book could tell the whole story—but isn't that always true, of every story? In its simplest terms the Holloman Story is the story of Holloman's uniqueness—the things that could only happen at Holloman.

But it was many months and stories later before the writer knew that.

2

TARGET FOR TOMORROW
Tracking a Hot Run

THE TRIMLY BUILT LIEUTENANT COLONEL with the iron-grey crew cut who bossed the information office strode from his small cubicle and paused at my desk.

"Got your pad and pencil handy?"

I looked up quickly and nodded.

"Let's go then." He grinned. "They're launching an XQ-4 and knocking it down with a Sidewinder and tracking the mission from King-One."

Inwardly I quaked. It was my first countdown.

On the way outside to the polished blue staff car he introduced me to the few others he was driving to the scene at the King-One tracking station. They were local newsmen. The Alamogordo daily's science editor. The El Paso AP man. The stringer who roamed the state for LIFE Magazine. All old pros! Politely they accepted me as just another newsman.

During the ride out along flat paved desert roads, past the low Holloman buildings, under the burning early morning sun, the tallest object in sight was the 150-foot bright red Aerobee tower which leaned a few degrees off vertical like a more famous tower at Pisa. Among the group the talk was as casual as gossip about the weather—but it was all missile talk. I listened and thought of everything I had learned about Holloman and its surroundings during those first crowded weeks.

When the first A-bomb worked its strange chemistry over the earth of Trinity Site to fuse it into jade- or turquoise-colored "glass-sand" (now called trinitite) there wasn't much around the Alamogordo Army Air Field if one didn't count the quonset huts and tents. Now the wooden buildings and structures of stone and brick, family quarters, ramps, runways, test stands, laboratories and other such features are too numerous to mention. And not only have they changed the Holloman skyline; the expansion has altered all the surrounding regions.

The town of Alamogordo a few miles away has grown from a whistle-stop on the Southern Pacific Railroad to a city of 25,000 holding many Holloman people. A new airport handles daily commercial transport service. From El Paso, Texas, 85 miles to the south new power lines have furnished more electric current. A pipeline from Bonito Lake 73 miles away backs up the Holloman water supply. Some 63 miles of fencing, 26 miles of drainage systems, 800 miles of paved and unpaved roads, government-owned or public domain lands involving $86 million in leased ground and facilities and over $65 million worth of equipment have all added their bit to the year-by-year process of making the Holloman area as complete a research site for its own specialized purposes as any in the world today.

However, except for its few fringe cities and sparse ranchlands, the area itself is lost and hidden in a wilder immensity, the Tularosa Basin —a vast open wasteland where the Great American Desert seems to stretch everywhere into naked infinity. (To be sure, the only true infinity is straight up; for the rest the Basin is bordered by the San Andres Mountains on the west, the Sacramentos on the east, the Rio Grande and old Mexico to the south, while Albuquerque, the largest city in the state, stands about 200 miles off to the north.)

Within the Basin's 6,700 square miles (actually an extension of Mexico's Chihuahua Desert) the typical picture is of scrub vegetation, mesquite, yucca, prickly pear, sagebrush, reddish brown earth—and cracked and parched river beds "ninety-nine and nine-tenths per cent" dry. The population density is about three persons per square mile. In contrast the density on the missile range during activity is five persons—and the state density still remains about eight.

All this of course is ideal for launching and catching missiles. But there is one startling contrast to the Basin's usual scrubby look. Like a beauty spot on the face of a dried old harridan the National Park preserve known as White Sands, just to the west of Holloman, spreads its snowy white dunes in fantastic soft patterns, drifting through sun and shadow, forming and reforming under the wind's wandering way, copying winter in summer and painting itself at sundown with all the pastels of the palette. Now a world-famous tourist attraction, it covers 224 square miles of the Basin and offers a creative mystery more fascinating than the stuff it's composed of—which is nothing but pure gypsum. (Which in turn is nothing but calcium sulphate—used for plaster of Paris!)

It was from this piece of gorgeous natural scenery that the White Sands Missile Range got its name.

Once the name was White Sands Proving Ground. It was an Army name, given in the early days of postwar missile experiments, V-2 rockets, Redstones, "Operation Paperclip" which brought in von Braun and his Peenemunde associates as partners in the Army's first groping efforts to open up the frontiers of space.

The Army is still here. So is the Navy. Both on the western edge of the range as the Air Force is on the eastern. The Army still administers the range and is responsible for all its scheduling activities. But now it administers for the Department of Defense and the range is a national range, the largest, most elaborate, overland tracking complex the free world has ever known.

From its first small areas of scrub earth where thirty-two V-2 and other rocket firings were accomplished in 1946 has been developed a 40- by 100-mile corridor now handling over 2,000 firings every year.

The corridor is also the most highly instrumented piece of real estate of its size anywhere in the nation—or for that matter, perhaps anywhere.

From one end to the other its Army-administered equipment and facilities include over 1,100 active instrumentation sites and 1,200 survey points. On and around the range a complex of high-precision instruments, both optical and electronic, gather data from every test. An integrated trajectory system, long-range cameras, powerful telescopes, telemetry stations, the most advanced radar equipment: all these form part of the great tracking network. Among the connecting links are 1,163 miles of roads, 60,000 miles of wire and cable, 340 microwave and radio channels.

Moreover there is a land addition to the range's regular 4,000-square-mile corridor—a 1,600-square-mile extension stretching almost to Albuquerque for the use of missile recovery crews.

However, the incidents requiring such out-of-bounds recovery are so rare as to be almost nonexistent. Basically this is due to the instrumental miracle known as flight range safety. Since every mission is tied in with the range's main control stations as well as its smaller units built like an electronic mesh all about the great range, every flight at every instant is being tracked, vectored, directed and monitored so closely that the slightest deviation can be immediately noted and acted upon.

Such precise tracking control not only provides the most precise kind of data collecting but in many instances allows the missile itself to be retrieved—one of the most valuable bonuses to overland testing, since it is often true that more can be learned from the missile than from the data.

In the same way unmanned target drones which act as sitting ducks for the missiles (or rather flying ducks!) can also be launched and re-covered. For instance, at the Holloman side of these electronic aerial skirmishes a Q-2C or an XQ-4 drone might be sent up to pit itself against any of a dozen types of deadly birds, its instruments set so that a near miss can be scored, the King-One tracking station busy vectoring and controlling the entire hot run, and in the end the drone floating gently to earth to be used in another series of air weapon tests.

It was such marvels as these I had heard about as I passed the King-One building time and again, squinting up at its roof where the dish-like antennae resemble giant Martian ears (to judge from the usual science fiction). Every so often men were on the roof too, swinging the ears from here to there—listening to what?

But they were not listening (as I was soon to discover) except to normal directions issuing from within the building, into their headset phones, as they calibrated the saucers against the control room instruments.

What were the instruments, then? And the other facts of this mysterious "vectoring" affair going on inside? While the questions still raced through my mind the colonel led our little news group into the building, past the watchful security police, to the crowded center room—and immediately there was the excitement of the mission itself.

"Just be the eyes and ears of the Air Force," he said to me. "And ask anyone here about anything."

I took a deep breath and tried to imagine I was just that.

In the massive-sized central room with its overhanging observation balcony, many men are huddled around the main control console—a square chest-high cabinet built like a four-sided coffee bar. They study the large plotting board in the center, where two stylus-like needles are moving just above, but not touching, the board. The needles, like sharp index fingers at the end of long metal arms, move fitfully—connected with the radar saucers on the roof outside. The lined and intricate radar map on the board shows the immense rectangle of the White Sands Missile Range.

The mission is under way. To launch a supersonic target in midair and kill it with a supersonic missile launched in midair. With the kill guided electronically from the King-One tracking station. Already a great bomber is circling the skies outside, the target drone nestles under one of its wings, a sleek jet craft watches alertly from near the bomber, another jet poises on the flight line far below ready to take off with the deadly missile. The men around the console are directing this kill. (Some of this I gather from the general talk, some the colonel patiently explains.)

The stocky young officer in command of the drone and its mission is also the beeper pilot—with the job of sending it through dives, rolls, climbs, turns, every elusive maneuver possible on its hot run.

Next to him stands his Operations sergeant, calling off his check list, calling the men in the skies outside, vectoring in the drop plane which is to launch the drone, also the chase plane now flying safety on the drone.

Another noncommissioned officer, lean-faced and dark-haired, in charge of the missile crew, hovers at an adjoining plotting board-and-console ready to vector in the drone on its hot run and the supersonic jet fighter which is to launch the missile. A civilian engineer monitors the radar beacon in the target drone to make sure it responds to every beeper signal on its hot run. Still another sergeant scribbles busily in a notebook, logging the entire chronology of the mission.

An Army man, the King-One plotting board operator, studies the stylus needles on both consoles more intently than anyone and manipulates his multi-knob control panel to make sure the needles keep operating.

The civilian range safety officer divides his time restlessly between the two consoles, ready to give the commands that will cut down the drone should it begin to stray, destabilize, or go wrong in any other way. A contractor technician is also on hand, from the aircraft company who built the drone, ticking off his own checklist, talking into his intercom, taking up technical points with the beeper pilot in charge of the mission. Elsewhere in the large room other men are doing other things. On the balcony a dozen more lean over the rail staring down at the central huddle.

The complexity of the operation is bewildering. Most of the men around the two consoles are wearing headphones. At times four or five are talking at once. The stylus needles flick over the plotting boards moving closer together on each board (duplicating the sky copying). The beeper pilot handles the short control stick in his beeper box— identical to a box in the drone with the same radio frequency making it a "ghost pilot" to follow his selected maneuvers. He studies his panel indicators showing fuel pressure, rpm, radar altitude, air speed, pitch attitude, roll attitude; all clearly marked. Questions, signals, reports pour in through the intercom sets or specially rigged telephones. Each control group tersely exchange their own items of information, communicating with the outside, timing and coordinating the flight movements. The talk is like a cypher zeroed into an enigma, except to the operators themselves . . .

"Pick up the count at three point four point eleven."

"Okay, we're standing by at three four seventeen."

"Tell the B-50 to slow down, it's proceeding too fast."

"Chase plane, we'd like you to chase four and a half minutes and be climbing all the way."

"The B-50 is banking thirty degrees right."

"Check off thirty-six and thirty-seven on your list."

"We're having trouble with the radar."

"Let's resume count at three four twenty-seven—okay and Roger."

"Check off forty, forty-one, and forty-two on your list."

"We won't go unless the radar straightens out."

"We are holding on the drone launch!"

"The radar has improved."

"Picking up the count at four point zero now."

"X minus six minutes on drone launch."

"Check off sixty and sixty-one on your list."

"So far so good on the radar—Roger."

"Make that rollout at three, four, five degrees, buster."

"Attack plane, fifteen minutes on engine start."

"The radar's poor, we can't take it like this. Hold for thirty seconds, give him thirty seconds."

"We can give him a minute and a half."

"Okay—the radar has improved."

"X minus three minutes on drone launch."

"Keep monitoring that beacon."

"Beacon's okay, Roger."

The needles move still closer.

"X minus one minute on drone launch."

". . . four . . . three . . . two . . . one . . . zero . . . *launch drone!*"

"Joe's picked it up on his plot."

Suddenly everyone's eyes swing to the second plotting board where the missile sergeant now handles the drone and the attack plane poised for their hot run. As the vectoring agent, his own part is to guide the missile-launching attack plane in the skies outside to a favorable position for a kill on the bomber-launched target drone.

(Vectoring: a problem of interception in which the speed and direction of the object to be intercepted is the first calculation while the second is the speed and direction of the intercepting object from a given point in space at a given instant of time.)

His vectoring accuracy can be observed from the two stylus needles above his own board. The needles are close together now.

"We are X minus two minutes on the hot run."

"On course, on time, she looks good, Harry, hold her where she is."

The missile sergeant leans over intently using a pair of calipers.

"King-One to attack plane—you are two minutes on the hot run. Vector starboard for a heading of three-four-five degrees."

"He's holding."

The calipers are used rapidly again.

"Attack plane—five degrees starboard."

"King-One from attack—I have a tally-ho on the target!"

"Roger—you are ninety seconds on the hot run. Go into afterburner. Vector two degrees starboard. *Missile away!*"

Every pair of eyes around the board is staring at the two stylus needles. The needles move still closer, the radar-controlling beeper pilot operates his stick from the first console, in the unseen skies outside the diving, turning, twisting, rolling flight-and-pursuit goes on, the needles move.

They come together.

And as suddenly the tension is over—both console groups go on with their checking but in a more relaxed mood, fresh cigarettes are lighted, the talk is normal and touched with laughter, everyone is in high spirits. (Oh the marvelous mysteries of electronics!) Even through the complexity it's plain to see that another mission has been a success.

Or to give the bare details: an XQ-4 supersonic target drone has been launched from a B-50 bomber, chased for safety by an F-100 jet interceptor, and killed by an air-to-air Sidewinder missile launched from an F-104 interceptor. (The kill has been a precalculated near-miss to save the drone.)

Meanwhile in the skies outside the pilot of the F-100 North American Supre Sabre chase plane has long since cleared the range and is now zooming back to the Holloman flight line. The Boeing B-50 drop plane has also cleared away and is coming in for a landing.

The Sidewinder carrier pilot who launched the deadly drone-finding missile streaks rapidly downrange in his F-104A Lockheed Starfighter to be clear of the next mission scheduled for the same wide, clean sky spaces.

And in the scraggly desert floor below, somewhere in the White

Sands Missile Range, the killed XQ-4 floats gently down under its three-stage parachute system and inflated landing bags—to be recovered, reconditioned, and used for another game of aerial tag on another day.

3

DRONE MISSION

In the Wild Blue Yonder

But far more of a thrill than tracking a hot run from within the King-One radar station was that of going on the hot run itself, though one came about as casually as the other.

"If you'll visit the target branch in our Aircraft and Missile Test Directorate and see Master Sergeant George Shute you might get to fly on a Q-2C Firebee drone-launching mission," our crew-cut colonel told me one day.

Thirty minutes later I was in that part of Holloman known as the West Area—a mighty scene of immense hangars, wide concrete ramps leading to wider runways, scores of moving or anchored aircraft spotted here and there, sleek jet fighters, cumbersome cargo planes, a few ungainly helicopters ("choppers" as everyone called them). Noise and confusion and activity where one had to pick his way as cautiously as any tenderfoot first confronting the Old West. The "Old West" was all around the area: vast expanses of plain and desert, purple and gold morning colors, low mountain ranges shimmering off in the distance like shadowy boundaries of nothing.)

I found the hangar in which the target branch carried on its administrative and technical duties. Master Sergeant George Shute turned out to be a tall, dark-haired, sun-tanned chap as genial as he was efficient.

"Try that on for size," he was presently saying, and I found myself in a bright orange flying-suit that might have been made for me. From the same corner in the small locker room he fished out a parachute harness.

"Have you ever been airborne?" he asked me whimsically and I was glad I could say yes. (Thinking of the many bucket seats and even parachute packs that had been my anything-but-unhappy travel lot in Europe—yet not even then quite like this anticipatory thrill.)

"This is Johnny Morris's gear," he said as jokingly, "but since he's on TDY travel I don't guess he'll heckle us."

In the electronic room which was another cubbyhole in the big crowded hangar building he introduced me to his four special co-workers. All, like himself, master sergeants. And all, as he said, airborne launch controllers. (A title I hardly caught the significance of then.) Joe Boyer. Johnny Shelton. Harry Sappington. George Leatherman. Was it an accident they were all big rangy men? Apparently. But more than that, what an efficient-looking crew as they strode outdoors in their bright worn flying-gear.

On the ramp again we moved toward one of the largest aircraft in sight, a ponderous thing, low, squat, almost too heavy to get off the ground as it seemed. This was the drone carrier.

"But it does get off and then some," said Shute. And I learned that with its four 3,750-horsepower turboprop engines and 132-foot wingspan this 108,000-pound monster, a C-130 Hercules, could carry 20 tons of cargo at speeds up to six miles a minute—and keep going for 2,000 miles without refueling. On an outboard pylon under each of its flat straight wings nestled what looked like a bright red missile—the two Firebee drones. Two inboard pylons also were visible, but empty today. Within each gaudy drone (as I was told) its shell was packed with electronic devices that would let it be air-launched, flown, controlled, guided high over the missile range as a target for an actual missile, and either killed or else scored against by other electronic calculations so that it could float down to the range under a parachute system of its own and later be repaired and used over again.

"In fact, it's nothing but a flying test bed we use to evaluate our aerial weapon systems," added the sergeant.

I was introduced to the aircraft pilot-instructor Captain Alan Swanson from Holloman's flight operations, to the co-pilot Major Bill Romansky, to Lieutenant Frank Wellin who would act as engineer-observer during the two drone launches. As we climbed aboard just behind the cockpit, I was again reminded of numerous military flights, noting the vast stripped-down interior, the supply of parachutes stacked neatly, even the familiar bucket seats where we were soon strapping ourselves down for takeoff. Through the big belly of the aircraft (where a rear door and let-down ramp could be operated to drive one or several vehicles inside) the compartment had been modified to hold an assortment of highly specialized equipment: racks of communication and telemetry instruments, radar units, computers, readout panels, also two large launch consoles, one by a port and one by a starboard window in the C-130's bailout doors, from which each right- or left-side drone launch could be completely controlled.

"This particular C-130 is a specially modified job called a DC-130," Shute genially explained. (He had said he would be too busy to explain later.) "It's also known as the Air Force's universal drone launcher. It can carry up to four drones at one time. It's also equipped with its own microwave command guidance system. That's the MCG hardware you see up forward there." A casual thumb pointed it out. "With tracking radars, transmitters, a flock of instruments that record drone flight performance. With this MCG system we're like an airborne King-One station, you know—we can direct the whole drone flight and hot run from here. Or we can use it as a relay linked in with a ground control station so the flight can be directed from there. As we're doing at King-One today, for instance."

I felt that I was getting to know all the Holloman operations.

While he was talking, the roar of the motors had started, every vibration seemed to quiver under our seats, the plane began moving, blue sky and building tops wheeled by in confusing small glimpses. At their respective launch consoles George Shute and Joe Boyer became a bit busier, phone headsets in place, starting the checkout that would prove the two drones' complete electronic systems and make sure of a "go" condition before it was time to go. The C-130 taxied for a long while. Stopped for a long while. The motors revved without letup. Suddenly there was a deeper roar, more intense vibration, movement and speed, more speed, a rapid crescendo of power and struggle throughout the huge aircraft. Then a lift, a lightening, a smooth long rise.

And we were airborne.

What a delight to be in the air again—almost a divided thrill from the excitement of the mission itself. Seat buckles were unfastened, crew members moved, the mood was an alert but easy one as the plane climbed, circled, climbed again, settled into a steady 180-knot flight due north along the Tularosa corridor which included the White Sands Missile Range, so clearly defined, with the low mountain ranges on either side now far below. On my own watch I had noted our takeoff

time: 10:05 a.m. Through the starboard hatch window the city of Alamogordo swept into view, a geometric pattern of clean straight lines
and squares almost reaching into the Sacramento foothills, with a grey-
black ribbon of highway running north and south from its western
edge, paralleled by the Southern Pacific railroad tracks. A few moments
later the vivid green blot that was the town of Tularosa lay below, separated like the oasis it was from the vague desert all around. What a
wonderful panoramic sweep as if from the eye of an eagle again! Stray
tufts of cumuli drifted by lazily, distantly, at little more altitude than
our own; the snow-capped peak of "Old Baldy" (12,000-foot Sierra
Blanca) reared above deep rough terrain that formed one boundary of
the missile range; the flat basin below us (full of arroyos and dry river
beds) made a medley of dirty-colored patchworks which, from the port
window, could be seen ending at glistening White Sands and the jagged
black slashes of the San Andres Mountain ridges. Steadily the four powerful motors droned onward—and one had to think again of why we
were there.

But the drone launch crew was already doing that—and other things.

The long checkout was still going on. At the hatch window on each
side of the plane stood a scanner. At each of the two launch consoles
sat an operator or controller. Each console controlled one launch operation, from start to finish, at one time. Each check was for possible malfunction at any time. The controller sent commands from his launch
control panel to the drone outside—and watched his panel meters for
electrical responses. The scanner watched the drone itself and reported
to the controller the drone's mechanical responses. Through such com-
mand-and-response processes the whole delicate, intricate checkout
task was going ahead; each drone's wings, rudders, elevators, all its
movable or working parts being rigidly tested. Likewise parachute systems and release mechanisms.

The lieutenant also pointed this out.

"For example if a drone's recovery chute ever popped out too soon
from its tail cone," he said, "the drone itself would have to be released
and dropped in an instant to prevent an aircraft nose-dive. Because no
crew member could escape by his own chute while the drone's chute
still billowed outside!"

It sounded like so hazardous a prospect that even the reporter found
himself watching more alertly for a while.

And suddenly something happened that seemed hazardous: the aircraft itself veered over sharply, made a steep bank, causing the quickest

kind of handholds, also the pit-of-the-stomach feeling of any ride down a roller-coaster. Then again. And again! What was *happening?*

"Lose two and gain four hundred . . ."

It was Shute talking. Asking the aircraft commander for dives and climbs for roll gyro displacement tests, then for pitch tests—some of the more turbulent motions of flight. By this time everyone had a head-set on; the intercom talk was like a counterpoint against direct talk. The dive and climb maneuvers were to check out the drones' moving assem-blies again. The lose-and-gain request meant that the aircraft should descend 200 feet and then climb higher. The drone sensors would lose and gain also—and thereby test such effects on the drone elevators. (All this was explained by the obliging lieutenant, though the commands themselves were too unintelligible for any new drone watcher.)

There were other checks being made. From time to time the aircraft commander's voice could be heard in the intercom as he ran through exact time signals with the King-One ground control station and then synchronized each with the launch controllers. A flick of a switch on the launch control panel was enough to tie in audibly with the aircraft's transmitter-receiver radio. Intermittently there were other voices, King-One voices, to be heard. (And what could a new drone watcher do then but think back vividly on the King-One part of such operations! Where the vectoring would be getting under way, the beeper box maneuvers too. Already we had seen a sleek F-100 chase plane slip by outside, ready to follow a drone right through its hot run. A missile-launching jet interceptor, perhaps two, would soon be starting a swift climb into these same skies. And now the entire aerial-and-ground picture was at least a bit more clear.)

At exactly 10:30 by the time signals the C-130 banked and turned sharply until it was heading due south again. A periodic countdown was issuing from the King-One station, permitting each drone launch controller to carry on an exactly timed event-sequence that would launch a drone at an exact instant.

At 10:40 the big aircraft headed southwest toward the glistening long rectangle far, far below that was the White Sands Missile Range. Controller Shute operated his launch console while scanner Harry Sap-pington watched the starboard drone. Everyone else watched the con-sole operation. The C-130 plodded steadily on. (In fact steady enough for a writer and his pencil and notebook.)

"Heading two by two."

"Speed one forty knots."

"Altitude five point nine." (About 31,000 feet.)

"X-minus seven minutes on first drone launch." (A King-One voice.)

"Start drone engine."

A touch at the right-hand launch console turned on the small but powerful turbojet engine inside the starboard Firebee, which would boost the drone to near-sonic speed a few minutes after launch. The 100-per-cent power run-up now was a final tryout, I learned.

"X-minus five minutes on drone launch."

"Change to internal power."

Another touch at the console detached the umbilical connection through which the Firebee was getting power from its C-130 mother aircraft, and turned on its own power.

"X-minus four minutes—"

The drone's four-channel telemetry system (through which it could be controlled remotely for rolls, dives, turns, altitude, speed, and parachute recovery) was also switched to internal power.

"X-minus two minutes—"

"Set off smoke trail."

A thick plume of white smoke began pouring from the wing of the C-130, billowed backward, became an endless tail.

"So the ground observers can spot us better," said the lieutenant.

"X-minus forty-five seconds."

Commander Swanson brought his aircraft to a straight and level flight.

"X-minus forty seconds."

The gyros inside the drone were uncaged and elevator settings adjusted.

"Fifteen seconds."

All external power to the drone was shut off completely.

"Four . . . three . . . two . . . one . . . drone away!"

The Shute voice was taut. His hand at the panel punched a button. At the same instant the drone under the right wing disappeared. The time was exactly 10:49.

But the countdown was still going on for the left-wing drone. All attention turned to the left-hand console. Now it was controller Joe Boyer and scanner Johnny Shelton handling the operation. Once more the final launch preparations were gone through: drone engine started, external-internal power switched, telemetry turned on, signals coordinated with the ground station, the Holloman flight tower, the radar and recovery units. The moments ticked off. The seconds fled.

"Drone away!"

The time was 10:59.

"Each drone is dropping a thousand feet a minute for two minutes," Shute explained easily, looking like his genial self again. "This gives it plenty of time to stabilize. It belongs to ground control as soon as it leaves us. They fly it on its predetermined course, zoom it up to altitude, vector it in for its hot run—and powie!" He spread his hands wide open and downward, looked whimsical again, grinned. Then listened within his phones once more.

Through the intercom connections could be heard some of the faraway ground chatter, still holding us within the magic circle.

"He's picked up the target on his plot."

"We're X-minus two on the hot run."

"On course, on time."

"F-106 ten degrees starboard—go into afterburner."

"It's tally-ho on the drone!"

"Vector three degrees starboard."

"Chase plane F-100—we'd like you to chase the second mission and keep climbing all the way."

For a brand new drone watcher it was only an electronic picture again. Yet not really too hard to imagine that diving rolling twisting drone-and-missile chase going on somewhere in the skies outside.

As we flew homeward I learned more about the five airborne launch controllers themselves. (Each one could handle any part of the launch operation; they were all controllers.) What a wealth of training and experience they had gathered to master a target drone's electronic complexities and that "on course, on time" result!

Collectively or individually all five had been working in missiles since about 1950. George Shute had been the first man in the Air Force to launch an X-Q4 supersonic drone. (A type the C-130 also carried and launched.) He had also gone through a batch of service schools in electronics, studied the same subject at Keio University in Japan, put in a flying tour on Guam, became part of a research and development drone squadron for the 1951 H-Bomb tests at Eniwetok, and completed an assignment in Europe with a Matador tactical missile combat team. Joe Boyer, engine specialist as well as controller, had worked for years with Harry Sappington on early Q-10 and Q-19 drones before moving on to Q-2 Firebees and Q-4 supersonic types. He had also been part of a technical group (with Shute) who ground-launched the first Q-2 Firebees and air-launched the first Q-4 drones. Harry Sappington had been a beeper pilot in the days when B-29 crews were still shooting down an earlier-type drone, the OQ-19, with live ammunition. (But he could just as easily have qualified for the shooting operation, having been a turret gunner on a B-24 Liberator in one of the most famous of World War II air raids—on the Ploesti oil fields in Rumania.) Johnny Shelton, a Navy World War II radar operator, had started his missile career with a Tarzan bomb group as a radio control bomb repairman, become an auto-pilot technician on some of those same early B-29 flights, gone into range instrumentation for a while, and had flown as a direct control operator in B-26 bombers dropping early types of target drones before the C-130 became a drone launcher. George Leatherman, who in addition to other talents was a missile checkout technician, had learned so much about C-130 launch systems that he had designed a new console to check out the four drone pylons in far less time than with its original equipment. All five, I found, had completed jam-packed technical courses in special training schools—and all five had gained a kind of fame together when they launched more target drones than any other airborne crew at one of the Air Forces's most famous shooting contests: a William Tell air gunnery meet.

And yet even this wasn't all, the *ne plus ultra* undefined even yet. In fact the age of specialization in the modern world seemed, itself, to reach another dimension when I learned to my amazement that, so unique indeed was this airborne controller job, there were only five such fully qualified men in the entire Air Force Systems Command—and all five were here in this lumbering Hercules vehicle as we flew homeward!

4

THE LONESOME BUBBLE

Faraway Part of the Mission

I WAS READING every "space" book I could lay hands on. The cluttered shelves of the information office held some. Others could be found in the quiet air-conditioned high-vaulted library across the street (converted from the Holloman chapel when a new one had been built). Gaudy-jacketed volumes with the most exciting titles. *Men, Rockets, and*

Space Rats. Man in Space. Satellites. Countdown for Tomorrow. Breaking the Sound Barrier. Rocket to the Moon. This Way to the Stars.

This way to a world utterly new.

Like the periodicals also: *Missiles and Rockets, Aviation Week, Astronautics, Sky and Telescope, Spaceflight, Space Journal, Electronics World.*

All full of the most fascinating, in fact weird details. Beyond the terrestrial atmosphere space is absolutely black. At twelve miles, blood boils. At seven G's it is like liquid iron. Free-fall is a zero-G condition. The velocity pull out of gravity must exceed seven miles per second. The collision of a spacecraft with a one-ounce meteor moving 20 miles a second would obliterate the spacecraft. The chemistry of earth life is the chemistry of carbon. Blue sky color is caused by the scattering of the colder light rays. At absolute zero (−459°F) molecular action stops. Liquid oxygen is an oxidizer for rocket power. In space there is no sense of motion. In space all bodies are weightless.

All these, and a thousand other items. But more than items: the careful growth of an organized body of knowledge, added to from innumerable sources, checked and corrected and added to again, gradually adjusting men's minds to the almost incredible new frontiers, enlightening everyone who took the trouble to read, even the merely curious. Even writers.

In fact the writer had to know. So it was more than idle curiosity. Or even fascination. As a means of talking with project engineers, track technicians, balloon launchers, off whose tongues the expertise of their special trades rolled almost without thinking, while they wrestled with the deeper problem of how to explain exactly what they were doing and why and for what results (always a murderous problem to the actual doers)—the writer's advance information was not only essential to getting the story but the way of earning their respect, even gratitude, and getting even better stories.

But in the end it was the fascination that remained. One could not help being curious about everything going on at Holloman. Although it was the home of the Air Force Missile Development Center there were so many things even besides missiles! Flaming rocket sleds roared every day along the famous test track. Towering balloon bubbles glistened on the horizon and sailed off to look like toys. Chimpanzees sported in their cages or sat meditatively in their "space" chambers. The muffled roar of a shake-table test came from one building, from another the thumping clatter of a stratosphere test. Every sight and sound seemed as enticing as every other, the itch to know all of it at once was like the need of sampling each item on the Smorgasbord table before settling down to the main meal.

"That's a good way to get your feet wet," said the colonel. (Tacking and cutting with his own ready metaphors.) "You'll find stories here wherever you go. The rocket sleds, the balloon launches, the space chimps—perhaps they're the most colorful. But there are others. The public wants to know and should know what goes on at Holloman. After all, it's their money."

"Where do the stories go?"

"Into the Holloman newspaper, the Rocketeer. Mailed out as regional news releases, for the local news agencies. All after being checked for accuracy and security, of course. And on to our headquarters in Washington, the more important features, where they go out to the national media—press, radio and TV, semi-technical publications, general magazines."

"What about the news and magazine people who come here?"

"They get the story too. They're entitled to the same information you are—if they stay long enough to dig it out. We take them out to talk with the project people, same as you do. So if you write as well . . ."

I wondered if I ever would. But at least the curiosity burned. Just to go and see.

As the dawn came up like thunder over the jagged San Andres peaks its long vermilion streamers lighted up a hundred canyons, a thousand emptier spaces—and one lonely bit of human life where a few men were occupied with a balloon. They were not playing with it. The arid desert looked like anything but a playground. Nor was their balloon meant for a plaything. The chilly morning, the loneliness, the big unwieldy bag bellying softly along the earth—these told of a more serious purpose.

It was serious enough: the remote part of a veritable web of activities spinning far away in a tall gray cinder-block building at Holloman. There, men were also working, and had been since long before dawn. X-one day meteorological forecasts the day before had been favorable. X-two-hour forecasts had matched just a while ago. The flight trajectory had been plotted, the exact launch site selected, supporting agencies had been briefed.

Over the radio waves from the tall gray building to the balloon crew's mobile radio van (called "Easy Two" for easy identity) the two-way radio phones were fairly crackling with instructions. On the roof of the tall gray building a theodolite station had been manned to get azimuth and elevation angles during every ten minutes of flight. From the Holloman air strip a light L-20 plane had taken off and was tooling along casually to be ready for tracking the balloon from launch site to target area and directing the ground crews to wherever it came down. On the missile range a tracking and recovery vehicle (identity "Easy Six") eased along Pole Line Road near the target area, its theodolites set for balloon angling, radio frequencies tuned for signals from the tall gray building and the L-20 so that it could go into action like the retriever it was. And on a Holloman apron, pointed toward the runway, stood the sleek F-104 representing the purpose of all these preparations in the deadly Falcon missile now nestling under its fuselage.

Infinite calculations! Based on wind, weather, atmosphere, cloud formation, drift potential, flight distance, underlying terrain. For an amazing result: to float in to a target area eleven miles square a target-equipped balloon launched 80 miles away—and to have it arrive at a precise altitude and a specified time. Through wind and weather and every natural disturbance. For a potential kill from the air-launched Falcon.

Which brings us back to our story: the lonely desert at dawn, the men working to launch the balloon—and the writer on hand to write about it.

The "omniscient" view above might seem a bit fanciful without some explaining. Rather than Big Brother watching, it was all a matter of communications. I had already visited the tall gray building and its many people, the missile range, the hangars where missiles and aircraft were mated, the Holloman flight line. So now it was possible to work out the imaginative film strip of activities—because here at the edge of the desert, as at every other point in the web, the multi-channel radio or telephone talk was a never-ending gossip line telling everyone just what was happening at every site either stationary or moving.

Such was the closed-loop system of expert timing and maneuvering I had heard about in the information office and was now witnessing.

"Go out and see if it's all as good as they say it is," the colonel said. "Follow the launch crew, stay with them a few days, eat and sleep and work with them. And bring home the human story."

This had meant starting out with the crew itself. First reporting to the Balloon Branch and awkwardly introducing myself to the tall quiet fellow with prominent freckles and a Georgia drawl who turned out to be the crew chief, Technical Sergeant Jim Bragg. Discussing the situation. Finding him a bit dubious, not to say quizzical about the story end of it.

"You're welcome," he remarked. "But we do this all the time. Don't know what they mean about it being a story, rightly."

So I had stowed my typewriter and camera gear and warm jacket along with his own equipment and boarded the comfortable convoy truck, for the long highway trek to the town west of the missile range with the quaint name of Truth or Consequences.

T or C was rendezvous-point. A typical desert town of wide sun-baked streets, motels, gas stations, restaurants and bars, dust and heat and somnolence. Here the crew usually stayed a week at a time, starting out for their launch activities long before dawn, coming back each afternoon with the immense convoy of vehicles: heavy duty trucks, light pickup trucks, bomb service truck, helium trailer, launch arm trailer, radio van, a few passenger cars.

And so this chilly morning operation in the desert had started well before sun-up too, twenty-five miles away in T or C and hours earlier when we had piled sleepily out of the Buena Vista Hotel to the unmelodious shouts of the crew chief's "Rise and shine now—up and at 'em!" Like the seasoned campaigners they were, the crew had gathered their vehicles together, opened radio contact with the tall gray Holloman building, checked out the latest weather reading on their next launch, eaten hasty breakfasts at the convenient all-night Dixie Cafe across the street—and gone careening off through the darkness, a great lumbering caravan that was now spotted about the rough clumpy mesquite in a tight little pattern almost reminiscent of the Old West and its wary wagon trains.

But there the comparison ended—and all traces of the Old West. Thirteen men in olive-drab fatigues (a few already stripped to the waist now that the sun had come up) were laboring with material and equipment that would result in fully inflating the small glistening bubble, preparing the instrumentation, fastening the payload under its parachute, centering the load for takeoff, and releasing the balloon to go sailing up toward the range on its intended mission.

It was the busiest kind of activity. Two of the men, Ben Hansen and Pete Hoadwonic, gently worked the kinks out of the silver-tinted, cellophane-thin, polyethylene material as they unrolled it along the improvised launch pad, a narrow 50-foot strip of the same material which had been stretched out across the launch arm trailer and the cactus-strewn desert floor to protect the balloon from fatal tearing.

Near the launch trailer (a simply made heavy low cart with a pair of roller-shaped locking arms to hold the lonely bubble in place until the entire balloon was released to rise over the payload) Joe Farni and Art McCluskey sealed in one end of the bubble's glossy red inflation tube through which a small amount of gas had already been piped from the many-valved helium trailer nearby.

From his position on the launch trailer Arland Phillippy ("Flip" to all the crew) directed the inflation job as another section of the balloon was eased by slow degrees between the launch arm rollers.

Farther along the pad George Barsuaskis knelt to work more effectively over the clock mechanism in the cutter box that would be carried aloft with the 24-foot parachute to control flight time and payload cutdown—which could be done by closing the cutter-box circuit on a small explosive charge to rip away the load line in case the special radio-command cutdown system failed to work.

One of the heavy equipment operators, Willie Strode, had positioned his giant helium trailer alongside, and at the far end of the pad his co-worker Frank Nichols had maneuvered the massive bomb service truck (known as the BST) into its assigned place. Beneath the BST's now horizontally stretched crane arm, Forrest Timme and Al Horst carefully fastened flares to the two-wheeled contraption called the hasti-cage as it hung from the crane arm—flares that were the very heart of the mission, that would later be radio-triggered to act as "hot" targets for the heat-seeking Falcon high above the missile range.

Beyond the helium trailer in the Easy Two vehicle where the 24-volt generator made a steady irritating racket, Joe Sickman and Jim Picerno crouched at their phone panels, still checking command information concerning launch site, wind velocity, trajectory, launch time, target time.

And hurrying everywhere went crew chief Bragg—listening in on the radio talks, testing helium valves, directing the balloon layout, shouting for the instrumentation truck to come up beneath the crane arm, helping as its command package was unloaded for tie-in on the hasti-cage.

Thirteen men—as oddly assorted a crew as their names. Coming from such diverse places as Pennsylvania, Missouri, Massachusetts, California, the deep South. Now that I had bivouacked with them for a couple of nights (and in the Arizona Bar shared a few cool early-evening beers before turning in for the next morning's hectic upheaval) it was like being one more of the crew. (Though a green member still being supplied from their own rich stores of information.)

The best launch time was early morning before the winds came up. A breeze over five knots meant trouble, over ten knots double trouble, over fifteen knots plain havoc.

However, as they continued working now within their tight little vehicle pattern, the four-foot test balloon at the end of its nylon string fifty feet above Easy Two showed hardly any wind at all.

By this time the aluminum shock-insulated command package with its four-channel transmitter and receiving set had been readied for sealing, the cutter box likewise, the helium hose nozzled into the shiny red inflation tube, the lonely bubble smoothed out beyond its locking arms, the hasti-cage sufficiently raised on the long crane arm.

Patiently, with a sense of his added responsibilities, Jim Bragg had been explaining it all.

"This flight control pack here is right fabulous, you know." He pointed to the glittering aluminum-boxed command package, about the size of a small carton of groceries. "It was put together right in our own electronics shop. That's what they call in-house building—and it's chock full of gadgets. The radio transmitter gives out flight signals and the receiver picks up command instructions. There's also hardware to cut the balloon payload loose, like explosive squibs and a mechanical cutter. The control center and recovery units are tuned in on the balloon frequencies. Flight signals are picked up at the center and used with the theodolite readings to plot the balloon position. The tracking units lock on by radio compass and work by triangulation until they sight the balloon. Command signals can lighten the bag by letting out ballast or lower it by valving off gas. Either the control center or the recovery crews can cut the payload down, by a radio command or the special clock-timed cutter."

"How do you keep radio interference away from the command equipment?"

"Both the receiver and transmitter are crystal-controlled. Also the receiver picks up an amplitude-modulated signal. But we've still got to watch that signals are not blocked!"

He had let the talk run over his other responsibilities; now he snapped back into new action. There were mental calculations to be made. For instance ballast and helium requirements; payload mass against balloon volume to determine mission altitude; balloon diameter 39 feet; volume 45,000 cubic feet; gross weight 285 pounds; balloon weight 79 pounds; parachute weight separate from payload weight . . .

With pencil and scratch pad he figured it all out.

"Twenty-two pounds of ballast," came his shout. "Tie it in." (They were small bags of fine steel shot controlled by a barometric aneroid device that could release them at a certain altitude, also by radio command.)

His next shout came.

"Open five." (Five helium valves, to mix the gas more evenly—without temperature variations—before inflation.)

Easy Two's generator was still humming, the command instructions still coming in. But there was a shout from the van and the round red face of Sickman popping out.

"Five Able to Easy Two—we slide launch time twenty minutes!"

"Five Able" was the identity of the control room in the faraway gray building. (Evidently command calculations had run into difficulties of their own.)

The small pibal balloon tethered overhead began weaving to and fro. (The word was pronounced "pie-ball" and meant pilot balloon.)

"Wind's coming up," growled Hansen. "Let's go, Five Able."

"Tell 'em we have a hot pack," shouted Barsuaskis who was now at the hasti-cage. (Warning to everyone that the target package was prepared, that radio frequencies had to be avoided that might pre-fire the flares.)

"Easy Two to Five Able—" Now fifteen minutes to launch time.

Bragg scrambled toward the launch pad. "Stand by to inflate," he ordered.

With McCluskey at the helium trailer the largest group lined up around the lonely bubble. In the BST cab, driver Nichols started his motor, ready for a mad dash under the balloon that would let its payload rise properly. At the firing station on the crane arm, Phillippy shoved in a panel jack and sat tautly awaiting a later signal to free the hanging payload from its holding squibs. Bragg raised one arm.

"Crack it!"

With a hiss, the rushing helium shot into the shiny red inflation tube. The bubble filled, strained upward, tossed in the light breeze—restrained only by the launch locking-arms, protected from ground buffets only by human arms. In moments it was towering over their heads, hissing and darting like a leashed cobra.

"What a monster!" (I was thinking of kiddies' toy balloons.)

"Monster!" Jim Bragg looked scandalized. "Wait till you see the Manhigh balloons! As big and high as the City Halls you Yankees build."

"You're fooling." (I couldn't picture.)

"A fact! We'll be launching another soon—I heard through the grapevine. As high as a football field on end—and just as round when it gets upstairs. This little old thing?" He grinned. "You'd better be around."

It was something to look forward to.

There was a shout from the helium trailer.

"Inflation completed." The call was from valve-tender McCluskey.

Instantly Farni was knifing across the end of the shiny red inflation tube. In seconds he had it tied up like an umbilical cord.

"That fixes our baby!"

From Easy Two came Picerno's relayed command call. "Clear to launch!"

With a jump, Bragg was on the BST running board. "Release!"

Hoadwonic pulled at the dowel in the launch trailer's upper locking arm. The arm flew back in a reverse arc, thudded against its catch pad, and with a rush the silvery bubble went upward, dragging all its long slack and the payload after it. On the running board Bragg directed the BST in its dash to get under the dangling payload.

"FIRE!"

Phillippy pushed down his firing switch. The current ran out to the squibs. With a pop like a cap pistol's the payload dangled free of the crane arm. The thin nylon cords between the upper and lower hasti-cage rings went taut and looked like the struts of an actual cage—with the payload bird perched inside, swaying gently but flying upward.

"That does it," murmured Bragg, and mopped his dripping forehead.

Everyone was dripping. The sun which had made long vermilion streamers was now riding high into the heavens—over a land where it was not unusual to have 50-degree temperature changes between midnight and noon. The peaks to the east looked black and even more jagged. The tangled desert floor seemed to shimmer off in the distance under dancing heat waves. Far away in the sky a few buzzards wheeled. Nearby an alarmed lizard suddenly made a blur of motion slithering into a new hiding place.

But still the tension wasn't quite over. Would the flight go? Only the day before there had been other complications: one balloon bursting in too frigid upper air, another ripping on the ground when a crane arm wire snapped.

The gleaming white bubble became smaller and smaller against the immense backdrop of deep upper blue.

"She's mounting right and headed right," murmured Bragg, still squinting.

"She'll be over the range at X time," Hansen added confidently.

And then there was no further time for watching and lingering; all at once new commands were crackling through Easy Two's radiophones for the next operation.

"Five Able to Easy Two—Five Able to Easy Two. Take off for radar balloon launch eleven zero zero hours—twenty miles due north of present launch site."

Within thirty minutes all the launching gear had been gathered and stowed, tools collected, launch arm trailer rehooked to bomb service truck, helium trailer to heavy duty truck, every vehicle set in motion. Back over the scrub landscape on to the pitted wagon road—in every direction a scene just as empty.

But to the north waited another mission, and in a cloud of dust the noisy caravan rolled on. It was rough riding, hard work—and far away from exciting end results like kills and hot runs and all the thrills of flying the missions.

Yet so indispensable a part that couldn't one say the mission started here in the desert at dawn?

5

MAN HIGH

The Sky Looks Black From the Edge of Space

BUT PERHAPS THE MOST SPECTACULAR of all events taking place at Holloman (saving only John Paul Stapp's rocket sled rides) were the manned balloon trips out through space itself. And every year or two there was another.

In fact, if a fine distinction could be made between the spectacular and the glamorous concerning such events it would be the sled rides with their brutal force that fitted the first, leaving the second to suggest the almost lyrical aspects of one vast glistening bubble lifting man into his newest mythos, the cosmic Unknown. Surely the ghost of Daedalus must have watched with longing and envy. And many a modern airman too.

It was an ordinary Southwest morning like countless others when the Manhigh III balloon, taller than a twenty-story building, dazzlingly beautiful against the deep blue New Mexico sky, swept up from a Holloman runway for a 100,000-foot jaunt to the edges of outer space.

Within its sealed tinfoil-bright gondola—only a man-sized cylinder dangling underneath the balloon like an afterthought—rode a young Air Force lieutenant, Clifton McClure.

All night long he had been sealed in while the launch preparations went on. The capsule's entire life-support system and other equipment had been checked. At midnight, in one of the aeromedical buildings, he had been lowered inside the capsule, its normal air had been flushed away by an oxygen-nitrogen-helium mixture found better for space flight, he had breathed pure oxygen himself to drive the nitrogen from his blood and avoid the danger of "bends" in any rapid decompression emergency. Tightly clad in a pressure suit, sitting on a shock-absorbent nylon-net seat, surrounded claustrophobically by a mass of instruments and made more uncomfortable by many body sensors for telemetering his physical condition during flight, he had stoically endured the long wait in the building and then on the launch runway.

At 6:19 a.m.—the very moment the sun's first rays broke over Sacramento Peak—the sharp hiss of helium inflation had stopped. The giant balloon had stood there straight and tall and still. At that moment its immense bubble contained 27,000 cubic feet of pure inert helium, which would expand to three million cubic feet a few hours later at the edge of space.

At 6:25 a.m. the sealed capsule had been trucked beneath the dangling red inflation tubes and their glistening central creation. Fastened to the outside of the capsule were the many storage batteries that would keep its interior systems recharged to maintain a reasonably equivalent earth environment and also be used as ballast and dropped one by one, at the end of small parachutes, to prevent the balloon from losing precious peak altitude.

At 6:50 the capsule itself had lifted free of the truck, gently swinging under its own long parachute system, still looking strangely isolated in its very first moment of forsaking the earth.

And then it had sailed upward—one of the first prototypes for future manned space cabins, a forerunner for the Project Mercury capsules which would orbit the chimps and man himself through space.

The young lieutenant's long earthbound wait had ended.

Within moments the gondola itself could hardly be seen by the naked eye, and the great polyethylene bubble—with a skin as thin as the cellophane of a cigarette package—was only another "toy balloon." Within an hour it was sailing at 40,000 feet directly over Sacramento Peak. Within two hours it was at 65,000 feet thirty miles southeast of the Peak and only a shining speck in the infinity around it. Within three hours it was at float altitude nearly 100,000 feet high, and had drifted on a new course to within twenty miles of its launch point. By then it had lost its pear shape and, seen as an upside-down image under the crossed hairs of a theodolite lens from the balloon branch roof, appeared as round and silvery as a soap bubble.

For the rest of the morning and part of the afternoon it remained visible, drifting through nothingness in several directions, continuing until it was far north of its launch site—which was empty by that time anyway, the Land-Air cameras gone, the crowd of spectators gone, the newsmen waiting elsewhere, only a few vehicles still in sight, one of them the all-important communication van with its telemetry and special-frequency radios which had formed the final earthbound link with the lonely rider in the sky.

Now the van was empty too and its small command group had also taken to the skies, in a round-bellied C-47 equipped as an aerial command post, which droned steadily along high over the White Sands Missile Range keeping up with the balloon flight.

The command and project group—aeromedical officers, the Winzen Research experts, the few invited scientists sharing the experimental part of the mission—were the people most vitally interested or essential to what was happening. Aeromedical chief Rufe Hessberg. Lieutenant Colonel Dave Simons, the pilot of the Manhigh II flight the year before. Captain Eli Beeding, project physiologist. Captain George Ruff, consulting psychiatrist for any human stress emergencies. (All "space doctors.") Meteorologist Duke Gildenberg from Holloman's balloon branch, who had worked out the entire flight profile. Don Foster and Vern Baumgartner, Winzen electronic engineers. Lee Lewis, ex-Navy balloon expert now with the same company. Vera Winzen, a licensed balloonist herself, who had helped design the Manhigh balloons. Almerian Boileau, the scientist for sky-brightness studies, George Neilson, the scientist for astrophysics studies, Doctor Herman Yagoda, the scientist for cosmic ray studies.

(Only one was regrettably absent, Otto Winzen, even now lying half shattered in a hospital room from an accident in a Manhigh practice gondola two months before. At that time Captain Grover Schock had been the selected pilot for the Manhigh III flight; he had been in the basket-type sky car too. A freak mishap had plunged the car and both men a hundred feet to the ground, where Schock, with his throat cut almost from ear to ear, would have died in moments except for immediate and expert first aid by Master Sergeant Ed Dittmer, following the flight in a ground vehicle. Both victims were to be laid up for months before full recovery.)

As the C-47 kept droning along each one in the group had his special task, monitoring instruments, giving technical advice, planning the scientific investigations. Apart from the individual experiments there was the avowed Manhigh mission itself, which could be spelled out as "the investigation of human reactions under space-equivalent conditions with basic emphasis on psychophysiological areas of interaction."

The young lieutenant in the space capsule—writing his destiny not on the wind now but in still higher regions—was that "psychophysiological area" doing its lively interacting. He was also the remote observer and "eyes and hands and senses" of the science panel and all the space doctors for all they wanted to know or would have liked to know.

Among the many instruments surrounding him in his cramped quarters were spectral spot-photometers, cosmic ray scintillometers, oscillometers, tape recorders, portable cameras, light meters, devices to record climatic and altitude and pressure conditions and variations of conditions. Among the life-supporting equipment in the marvelously contrived capsule were oxygen and ventilating systems, an air regenerating system, insulating system, automatic-blower and air cooling system, plus secondary systems against failure for most of the primary systems.

From the communication van on the ground or the C-47 in the air there was also ingenious protection—in other words the most careful attention to the physical reactions of the capsule rider (the passive study-instrument) through voice or telemetry signals. Moment by moment the command group were aware of his heart beat, respiration, body temperatures, skin temperature, physical elasticity or exhaustion, blood and nerve response; also capsule temperatures, humidity, altitude, pressure, mechanical conditions. Within their own control was emergency cutdown instrumentation that could have freed the capsule from the balloon to float it down by parachute in half an hour.

Moreover the hermetically sealed capsule itself contained a release mechanism—and by using this the lonely sky rider could have escaped by his own efforts and descended by parachute.

Conditions had been fine for a while on the way up. The 25-year-old McClure had followed directions, working his instruments, working the Boileau spot-photometer, changing the Yagoda film plates, tape-recording his own feelings and impressions.

He also looked at the immensity around him and beheld wondrous things.

"I can see out of a porthole at a forty-five degree angle. I see a blanket like a halo or a glow from a fluorescent tube where the horizon should be—but I can't find the horizon. The halo is shaded into a band of blue like the normal sky. But a few degrees higher it fades into still deeper blue, and then ten or fifteen degrees higher into black, almost complete black—the black gets darker and darker—it's almost as if I'm *feeling* it—it is indescribable! Then as I look upward there's this huge brightly white balloon and completely surrounding it this blackness so much darker than what I used to think was black. I have the feeling that I should be able to see stars in this darkness but I can't find them either—I have the feeling that this black is *so* black it has put the stars out!"

Truly wondrous things—like the awareness of no-light in some strange pocket of God.

But other things too had been happening on the way up and then at float altitude—and only the group in the C-47 knew it. Or they and the sweating but spellbound sky rider. For he was sweating! After only that many hours the capsule temperature was registering 118 degrees—the highest its gauge could go. In the C-47 the consternation mounted. The reading was asked for again. Still the same. But it must have been wrong. The rectal temperature was called for. Over 101 degrees! The capsule rider himself complained of the heat—and his sluggish tones in the microphone confirmed what had been happening.

But what *had* been happening?

For one thing it seemed that the air regenerating system was not working properly. Carbon dioxide and water were removed from the capsule atmosphere primarily by chemical action. Air circulation through the system was controlled by a centrifugal blower taking air from the heat exchanger and circulating it through the air regeneration unit. The water-core heat exchanger was supposed to remove heat from the capsule at the rate of 1600 BTU's (British thermal units) per hour. The regenerated air was supposed to flow back into the capsule through a flexible two-inch hose and do its cooling.

Only, it wasn't.

When the perspiring capsule occupant, by this time more than a bit feverish, was directed from the C-47 to try cooling himself with the hose, he found that its air felt hotter than he felt himself!

And still his temperature mounted. From 101 . . . to 102 . . . a tired reading to the group of anxious listeners below, 104.1 . . . presently 105.2 . . . finally almost 107!

But long before this the command had already come from the C-47: "Valve off your gas and descend."

The complete capsule descent had been decided on as a safer way than allowing him to parachute down in his present condition.

Sluggishly he had accomplished the valving, following in slow motion the radioed instructions for operating the valve switch.

But now the balloon descent itself was deadly slow. For the helium in the giant polyethylene bubble was still expanding from the late afternoon solar heat. By this time the C-47 had landed at a small airport west of the missile range and its command group was signaling, directing the exhausted sky rider from there. They had other things to make them frantic also—the possibility of a night descent, and possible impact in the nearby mountains.

But the main worry was still the first one—the heat in the capsule that was doing the killing.

Meanwhile the news had been picked up from the balloon branch that the balloon was coming down prematurely. The planned flight had been for a minimum 24 hours. In the information office where most of the press and radio people were either lingering or wandering in and out, the reaction was immediate and electric. The office itself had been a hectic scene for the past 48 hours—like any newsroom anywhere as reporters and photographers kept showing up, wire service men, LIFE Magazine's local staffer, radio and TV people from El Paso, Air Photographic and Charting Service people from California, free-lance writers, wanting facts, wanting pictures, telephones, transportation arrangements to cover the launching, the air and ground sites, the expected impact site. On the morning before X-day a press briefing had been set up with McClure himself carrying the spotlight, answering scores of queries.

Now those who were still waiting wanted to know.

But all that could be found out was: "The cooling system isn't working." This the balloon branch did know. But the anxious people in the command group so far away were far too busy to think of "information" —understandably. One of them, Doctor George Ruff, had already taken off from the little T or C airport in a tracking helicopter, winging through the twilight to be where the capsule was expected to come down. But this also would only be known later.

So the long vigil went on, with the tight waiting in many places—in the C-47 now flying back toward Holloman, in the aeromedical buildings, in the information office—and a bit more tragically in a small backyard near Holloman where Laurie McClure, the young lieutenant's pretty wife, had watched all day through the McClure telescope with which they had followed the Moonwatch satellite programs.

Everybody knew *something* was wrong—but what?

The news came through that the capsule had landed. The time was almost seven o'clock, the range and all Holloman lay in new darkness. Reporters fled to their phones. Others clamored for further facts. It was known that a helicopter had done the recovering, some thirty miles north on the range, that the Manhigh rider had immediately been flown to the Holloman base hospital. The commander of Holloman's research and development activities, Major General Dan Hooks, telephoned the information office for positive confirming news and also for further facts.

Equipped with this authority—and while the information office chief held the news people at bay—it fell upon this writer to go to the hospital.

George Ruff was there, Simons was there, Hessberg was there, Vera Winzen quiet and preoccupied—and McClure himself, large and smiling and sitting up in his narrow hospital bed, clad in rumpled white pajamas.

One thing he said was: "I don't know what all the fuss is about." With a huge grin he added: "I just started to simmer, heat up, and boil all over." But the grin remained. And another thing he added: "I don't have to be treated like an invalid, you know." He was boyish about it and obviously healthy and embarrassed by the attention he was getting.

But he was "news" rightly enough—as were all the Manhigh pilots. Besides Simons, Captain Joe Kittinger (later to be of tremendous news interest in balloon exploits) had been a Manhigh rider the year before, climbing to 96,000 feet as the first "daring young man" in such experiments. Both he and Simons had achieved national fame through their flights. Thus young McClure was in distinguished company from the moment he had been selected as a Manhigh pilot.

And how *had* he been selected? What had it taken, in background training, aptitude, ability, character, to be chosen by the United States Air Force as a lone traveler to the edge of space?

Leaving him tired but clearly happy in the hospital bed (and leaving the information office chief at bay), the Manhigh III story was still Lieutenant Clifton McClure's story. George Ruff had said a thing about it. He had said: "Without his own determination and intelligence and *psychophysiological* stamina Cliff McClure would never have survived—and that's another thing Manhigh has taught us about selecting our astronauts."

One other remark McClure himself had made seemed just as significant.

"I was sure," he said, "a two-way ticket was attached to this journey."

It seemed he had made himself sure in many ways, including that priceless ingredient sometimes called dedicated faith.

All through his teen-age and young man years he had burned with it. Through books, studies, experiments, school and university life he had tracked his way into ceramics, electronics, astronomy, astronautics, celestial mechanics, and technical photography. At the Air Force ROTC unit at Clemson College near his home town in South Carolina he was corps commander in his senior year. There he also won the Air Force Association award and a Republic Aviation award for outstanding scholarship. At Bryan Air Force Base in Texas where he started his military career he had quickly become a jet pilot and then a pilot instructor. At Holloman the combination of flying and astronautical interests had again marked him as a valuable man for research and development work.

A vivid impression of him lingered in my own mind from a meeting which happened when he first appeared at the Aeromedical Field Laboratory. Big and stocky, friendly and eager, with hair a bit mussed as if there were other things to think about, he was reporting for duty with the Laboratory's sub-gravity scientist, Doctor Harald von Beckh. It was clear that he could hardly wait to begin.

"I'd like to get checked out in an F-94C right away." (He was referring to the aircraft then used for Holloman's zero G flights.) "I'd like to fly it and be a test subject as well."

That this was more than young man brashness was proved later when von Beckh was saying: "His ideas about Keplerian trajectories are excellent! Also on our electronic problems, our ground communicating." Later still it was von Beckh who labeled young McClure as one of the best subjects he had studied for the isolation and confinement tests even then under way for the Manhigh III pilot selecting.

Perhaps this was no more than to be expected of a lad who began his flying career at age thirteen in his dad's private plane and made his first solo two years later when his dad "wasn't looking." But could teen-age McClure have suspected anything of his future·destiny when he began observing Nature's flying experts by chasing in his light plane after migrating ducks? Probably not—yet by coming in at the back of the duck V and throttling down he learned that only the lead duck showed alarm, changed formation, even dived with his duck squadron as low as some tree tops.

"I wasn't afraid of clobbering in by diving after them," was his quaint explanation. "After all *they* didn't crash."

He also became a sailplane pilot. (A sailplane being a high-performance glider.) In fact he was still passionate about them. As a member of the American Soaring Association he had already ordered his own.

So what did it take to become a Manhigh pilot? But much more. His really grueling training hadn't even begun.

He went through psychiatric sessions that probed every facet of his behavior, response, personality. He took countless psychological tests such as the Rorschach ink blot and a long list of aptitude and intelligence experiments to measure his mental and sensory alertness. He took whirling centrifuge rides, heat box and icebox tests, physical and chemical tests of all descriptions. He entered Holloman's stratosphere chamber in a simulated Manhigh cabin environment and remained there 36 hours while emotional pickup, fatigue response, all his stress reactions were exhaustively studied. He sat in another soundproof chamber in claustrophobic darkness and silence for 43 hours. He spent weeks in the air learning to operate conventional-type balloons. He also made his first parachute jumps.

Working with the Manhigh invited scientists he spent many hours going point by point over every complex experiment and each instrument for it (not knowing that, regrettably, some of the experiments would have to wait for still further Manhigh flights).

So what had it taken?

Inevitably it had taken him away from many of life's human enjoyments—his personal hobbies, personal and private life. Time away from hunting and fishing, from books, photography, his favorite hi-fi. Time from a new young son and his pretty wife Laurie. Though here he had been lucky too, for Laurie was as keen as he on some of his hobbies. Together they charted the satellite programs, studied the star courses, discussed the future of space—and Time had become a conjointed and fluid thing between them.

Mix all these ingredients, add another dash of luck, much boyish friendliness, Johnny-on-the-spot availability, and certainly the united efforts of many other talented and earnest men—and perhaps that could be the answer to how Lieutenant Clifton McClure climbed from his modest place on earth to the second highest balloon altitude ever reached then in man's race toward the stars.

6

BALLOON RESEARCH
Science's Wonderful Skyhook

DURING THE LATE 1950'S AND EARLY 1960's the most spectacular balloon projects at Holloman were the Manhigh flights, the Excelsior project with Joe Kittinger jumping from the edge of eternity into world headlines, and the Stargazer project with Kittinger and Navy civilian astronomer Bill White riding a gondola all through the night—each project in its own way advancing the science of high-altitude balloon research.

And during those few years a lot had happened with the science of ballooning as well. How far away and primitive seemed the small "lonesome bubble" launched so long ago at the edge of the desert capturing the writer's imagination and leading to many further attempts at description.

Yet basically the launch and recovery methods were the same, if with far more refined equipment. Even the Holloman ballooners were mostly the same, the civilian technicians and weather experts, many of the military in ranks from airmen to master sergeants—all masters at last of balloon techniques, with a wealth of experience not really to be matched throughout the science world.

By the mid-1960's there were more than fifty seasoned experts who made up the launch and tracking crews, communications and electronics teams, with a hard core of old veterans filling in the top spots—Herb Markley as civilian chief, Duke Gildenberg as chief meteorologist, Dave Willard heading up the electronics, Milford Brown the communications, Bob Blankenship the recovery, two crackerjack master sergeants Melvin Johnson and Bob Donaldson the launch operations, besides Jim Bragg, Ben Hansen, Grady Cole, Blair Tenney, Fred Hanson, Earl Norris, Rod and Lonny Moss (not brothers); all together representing an experience-total as impressive as one of the towering balloons itself.

Long before that, too, the branch had gotten a name change, to the

Balloon R&D Test Branch, operated as part of the Air Force's Cambridge Research Laboratories.

And yet, apart from the people in research and development itself, plus a few prominent news headlines now and then, it would have been surprising if the public at large realized that even in the modern era of rockets, supersonic aircraft and ICBM's one of man's earliest flying-dreams—the balloon—was playing a tremendous part in the scientific progress of the Space Age.

The spectacular manned balloon flights were one thing but the quiet non-manned flights were just as much a thing. Through balloon research the earth's atmosphere up to about 25 miles was being explored far more thoroughly, for much longer journeys, at considerably less cost, than with any other type of space or flight vehicle currently in operation.

For example, probing rockets like the Aerobee stayed at peak altitudes only seconds at a time. Experimental spacecraft like the X-15 and orbiting Mercury and Gemini capsules flew seldom and needed months of flight preparation. Satellites like the Explorer had different research objectives involved with deep space penetration.

On the other hand the balloon flights produced veritable skyhooks in space and were almost as frequent as the days—for a variety of research almost too rich to describe. At Holloman they had been going on since 1947. In fact it was a surprise to find that the first balloon launch had preceded the first missile launch, occurring June 5, 1947, and sponsored by a New York University team. (With rubberized balloons only seven feet in diameter!)

Three years later, on July 21, 1950, the first launch with an all-Air Force team took place (with polyethylene plastic balloons by that time) using a comparatively small bag 72 feet in diameter to carry a 50-pound payload—though it did rise to 90,000 feet.

Since those really primitive beginnings the Holloman crews (up through 1965) had launched close to 2,000 balloons ranging up to 13 million cubic feet in helium capacity, over 332 feet in diameter, to altitudes as high as 134,000 feet, carrying payloads as heavy as 5,000 pounds.

Such were the dry statistics—but there were still the magnificent floating journeys themselves.

Besides the manned flights gathering information about rarefied atmospheres, subzero temperatures, cosmic rays, sky brightness, spectral phenomena, space capsule design, and biological hazards, there were the innumerable quiet flights loaded with exotic devices for studying missile reentry, dust diffusion, radio transmission, artificially induced sodium clouds, range instrument improvements, miss-distance indicators, nuclear blast fallout, rocket beacons, nose cone calibrating, parachute motion—and many, many more.

Since the "lonesome bubble" days several hundred of those same silvery target balloons had been wafted in over the range for missile practice. A capsule recovery program with 100,000-foot drops for stabilization studies had led to the first successful midair catch of a Discoverer capsule coming out of orbit. High-altitude drag balloons had been tested to slow up missiles, escape capsules, and other spacecraft zooming at reentry speeds far out from earth. Night flights with special camera equipment had been successful in collecting new photography of the moon.

There had even been a lighter side to the ballooning (no pun intended!) when some flights were staged as part of a Twentieth-Century Fox movie called *Threshold of Space* (featuring John Paul Stapp as one of its film immortals).

All of which had proved time and again that with science doing the inflating a balloon was anything but a mere bag of wind. Although meteorologist Gildenberg's sage observation had taken a different tack, for he was fond of describing each one he nursed through its weather profile as "only a profoundly engineered vegetable bag."

There had been other changes at the new Balloon R&D Test Branch. For instance an immense glass-enclosed room full of communication equipment, radar units, wall maps, weather charts, plotting tables, telephones, in short a complex covering the newest refinements in balloon operating. Linked with every tracking site on the 40- by 100-mile missile range, its networks were able to follow each balloon from takeoff to flight's end and control the payload recovery by command signals which detached the load and parachuted it gently to the ground.

For off-range flights its fast lines were also in touch with distant agencies, individual air traffic stations like the Air Defense Command, the Federal Aviation Authority, the Federal Communications Commission.

Based on a highly intricate communication system of its own involving hot phones and special radio channels, its incoming and outgoing information covered launch times, float durations, signal frequencies, identification signals, terminal forecasts, tracking procedures, recovery results, all flight data.

Another special feature was its weather station, the heart of the complex for its highly trained meteorologists. By "weather" all its flight forecasts were plotted taking in upper wind structures, cloud formations, drift potentials, time and distance objectives, altitude changes, underlying terrain, inflation and climb rates, hourly change reports—to produce almost uncanny accuracies concerning flight trajectories and expected impact sites.

The complex itself was known as the BCC or balloon control center. Literally, it was a tracking station. It was also the new Air Force agency charged with the 24-hour-a-day seven-day-a-week job of monitoring every balloon flight in the United States.

On every mission day (which was most days) the BCC scene was, to say the least, hectic. Always the bustle started long before launch time. (Since most launches were early morning events this usually meant midnight activity as well.) For instance the flight coordinator would be establishing his contacts with the launch site and synchronizing all timepieces by checks with Arlington WWV time signals. The meteorologist would be working out last-minute profiles directing the launch crew where and when to launch, the recovery crews where to move out toward predicted impact. A large countdown clock in the huge communications console ticked off its reverse intervals to transmit the countdown to all range stations and tracking and recovery units. A round green oscilloscope window in another console panel showed its endless light-blips by way of monitoring all command signals. (If the light did not blip, the signals were bad.)

In the midst of these activities the field test director (usually Markley himself) would be checking inflation figures signaled in by the launch crew chief, other reports showing whether the electronic controls were still working in the balloon's command control package. During the final minutes and seconds he called out a countdown over all speaking circuits and gave the actual command for "balloon away!"

At that precise point the balloon control center went into its tracking actions.

A computer-controlled radar plotting board monitored by Army technicians produced a visual plot of the balloon in flight, exactly as similar equipment at King-One and other range tracking stations provided a plot for a missile in flight. All flight directions came from the control center. Radio commands activated the valving and ballasting of the balloon to direct its physical climb and comedown. Radio control was also maintained over its command package (always a separate instrument unit from the research package). Thus a transmitter in the command package furnished directional information and in turn BCC signals operated the electronic devices to separate both packages for parachute descent. The network of hot phones or special-frequency channels provided continuous contact with all radar sites, telemetry stations, mobile recovery vehicles or tracking aircraft. Radio equipment in the ground vehicles or aircraft could also be made to control the flight and cutdown if directed from the control center. A special tone signal from the balloon's transmitter alerted recovery crews when the flight was over, and the transmitter's antenna, chuted down with the payload, continued its signal-bleats like a bellwether until the recovery crews closed in and did the retrieving.

Thus in less than two decades balloon science too had advanced— with Holloman as its proving ground—to a well-defined place in the Space Age. Compared with other activities helping to chart such regions, its practical workers, who got the giant "vegetable bags" off the ground and controlled each flight, were surprisingly few—there were not many Gildenbergs, Markleys, Johnsons, Braggs, nor such tracking and recovery crews to be found elsewhere in the multi-affairs of launching man toward the stars. One little detail of such real progress could have furnished its own example: the almost certain recovery of each valuable instrumentation package. As a carryover from early days the practice was still followed of marking every package on the outside with full identification and the offer of a cash reward for return by any random finder. During those primitive days, packages had sailed off as far as Norway, Sweden, Africa; several had been returned by natives deep in Mexico who carted them on muleback to the nearest railroad station; one had been personally delivered by a cowboy still loping on horse- back as he reached the Holloman gate.

But the last such "lost" package had occurred in 1955.

It was this skill and science that made possible what was perhaps the greatest ballooning feat and the greatest moment in the Holloman group's long list of such achievements—launching Captain Joe Kittinger in an open gondola for his twenty-mile leap through space and bringing him safely back again.

7

OPERATION HIGH JUMP
The Leap Into the Void

THE CONVOY ROLLED OUT through the Holloman gate just before midnight. Pickup and recovery trucks, helium trailers, flat-beds
carrying the balloon gondola and the crated balloon, communication
van, dressing van, red-cross van, bomb service truck (BST), trucks bearing immense generators, others with powerful searchlights, Land-Air
vehicles with their camera crews, launch equipment vehicles, air police
vehicles, radio and press cars, commercial TV vans, in roar after roar
passing the lighted gate where its lone guard blinked and then blinked
again. A convoy three blocks long as it rumbled through the night-empty
streets of Alamogordo, reached the open highway again, clattered
through smaller Tularosa, swung off the highway bearing east along a
winding dirt road, filed one by one into the abandoned Tula air strip
that was the launch site. Jack rabbits hopping out of the way. Sagebrush and mesquite and cactus on all sides. A horned golden moon
with both ends pointed up, just appearing over the horizon. Lights
appearing, giant searchlights hooked to generators, camera lights beginning to show. Millions of flying insects stirring and collecting in
clouds. Large black beetles crawling hastily over hard bare ground into
scrub and darkness again. Vehicles deploying in an orderly fashion,
gondola and dressing van at one end, balloon vehicles at the other,
spectator cars along the sides, police roping off the critical areas. The
narrow canvas strip being laid out the whole length of the field between
inflation point and gondola to protect the balloon later in unrolling.
The bomb service truck with its high crane arm in place, launch-arm
vehicle in place, men swarming around the balloon equipment, others
beginning the gondola checkout that would go on for hours. Small
rubberized weather balloons immediately released at various spots, pibals
sailing up into the dark, tethered and held, caught by the glare of
searchlights, shining with a fish-belly hue—one with its own attached
light-flare rising higher, mingling with a thousand star points, moving

among the points like a tiny Echo satellite (like the real one visible some nights before). In the midst of the work, the camaraderie. Coffee simmering in various vans, small huddles of men gathering briefly here and there, lone wanderers receiving hospitality—the warmth of talk and hot steaming cups taking the nip out of the frozen night air. But most of the picture men (like the balloon men and gondola men) already too busy. Land-Air setting up its large floodlights, fixing cameras on the roof of its main van, APCS men finding other sites, the National Geographic team, the TV crews, the free-lancers already covering all kinds of side-bars for their photo or feature spreads.

And still the long vigil continuing. Long before the arrival of its star performer who is to appear at two, move into the dressing-van, start his oxygen breathing two hours before launch time, start dressing— helped into his insulated porous underwear, partial pressure suit, heavily quilted underwear, winter flying suit, woolen socks and electrically heated socks, nylon-insert gloves, high-altitude pressure gloves, heated flying gloves, rubberized boots, pressure helmet—which together with his outside equipment and his own weight will make him a 313-pound Gargantua ponderously moving from van to gondola. For such is a part of the preparation necessary for a long leap into space.

The air grows colder. But it remains still, the pibals hardly move. Here and there a few lower stars blink out behind filmy veils of scud, the first faint not-ominous sign of "weather." Steadily the activity goes on. From the high BST boom dangle the shrouds of the red-and-white striped gondola parachute—to be fastened beneath the balloon with its small square instrument package that will explosively release the gondola after jump time. The electronic checks go on; telemetry circuits, safety plugs, radios, pre-set cameras, parachute equipment, valve controls, ballast controls. Around the gondola on its flat low trailer the tightly knit technical crew who have come with Kittinger himself from Dayton, Ohio, are just as busy. And time and again the camera people are there, capturing from all angles the one sight that seems to fascinate them most—the large printed words under the gondola's little gateway step which say: THIS IS THE HIGHEST STEP IN THE WORLD.

(Who has printed them there, foreshadowing events to come? But none other than the Holloman crew themselves, surely romantics every one.)

And the Man arrives! Brought by the pair who have personally awakened and escorted him, Ken Arnold and Frances Beaupre (both large parts of the project). But only a brief glimpse now of the Kittinger large freckled grin and invariable red hunting cap (luck charm in all his jumps) while the cameramen scurry. For all is in readiness in the dressing-van—air blower on, clothing and equipment laid out, Master Sergeant Daniels and Technical Sergeant Fritz there to handle the critical job of dressing, Captain Billy Mills as project officer, Master Sergeant George Post as backup jumper, Captain Marvin Feldstein and Captain Richard Chubb as flight surgeons. The National Geographic team Rowe Findley and Kurt Wentzel who are there on a pool basis for pictures to be available to all news media are also permitted inside. The door of the van closes, only its cheerful little window light can be seen. Disappointedly the other shutter-bugs turn away. But there are more things to photograph. More things to do. Instrumentation packages to assemble. Helium valves to check. Weather observations to make. More scud is in the sky, blotting out a few more stars, vaporizing the slender golden-horned moon. In the communication van, signals crackle between there and the BCC building far away. On the Land-Air van's built-up platform roof Bill Gross and some of his documentary film crew, Jack Mitchell, Bob Halferty, Tex Helm, catch the long scenes for establishing shots, climb down and hurry everywhere for the latest closeups, getting the technical coverage that will become master and work prints for the project people. While they are still at it the sound of motors is heard, lights blink in the darkness overhead, a pair of helicopters, vast whirlybirds with humming rotors, settle slowly beside the air strip, ready for their part of the tracking job when the time comes.

And then, disaster! The round unsmiling face of Billy Mills, behind a cigar clenched at a furious angle, behind words dropped like angry bullets. "*Launch time sliding one half hour.*" Rain already reported north on the range, a 14,000-foot overcast moving in, weather problematical in the jump area.

The slender horned moon totally disappears. Collective gloom spreads as black as the night. And just when it seems too inky, half an hour after the first report—restoration again! The Billy Mills face one vast smile, the words quickly scribbled on the van door: the mission is ON. The balloon truck rolling to the end of the long brown canvas strip, the crate ripped open, the red polyethylene gleaming as it unfurls along the strip. The dressing-van door opens and the gargantuan, over-burdened, bent-down figure of the Jumper appears, framed by the light inside, moving slowly among his faithful helpers, reaching the gondola trailer, the step, the basket seat itself. With the cameras really going mad. Air police watching the lines more alertly, where more and more spectators have arrived. And with them the dawn—pale sky in the east, black knifelike Sacramento ridges showing, desert shrubbery turning dark green. The day and Time Zero both approaching, the launch crew working fast, the helium hissing, Ben Hansen valving, Cole braced with the long inflation tube, Johnson hovering everywhere, the pear-shaped bubble lifting slowly, gracefully from the earth, glistening in the light, beginning to strain at its holding arm, becoming alive, restless, swelling with a mighty sound like the rushing of wind, larger and larger, towering over the scene dwarfing all its watchers, still straining at the end, the inflation over, the gondola moving in, the final fastenings made, the final commands given—and like a clap of thunder streaming out to its full length, lifting the gondola free, sailing rapidly up toward the cloud scud, under the dawn-blue sky, bearing the gondola and the man, the Jumper, small and lonely underneath, up toward greater loneliness, hazard, the unknown—and into splendor.

The takeoff time was 5:29 a.m. At takeoff the 3,000,000-cubic-foot balloon, made of polyethylene two-thousandths of an inch thick, began lifting its 1,050-pound gondola at the rate of 1,250 feet per minute. From the ground this climb rate was monitored with the greatest care; anything too fast would have created drag against inside pressure that could tear the light material apart. Several times on the way up the Jumper was signaled to valve off helium as a safety measure.

There was also danger at the tropopause level about 50,000 feet where 100-degree minus temperatures, the coldest of the trip, made the balloon so brittle it could again have burst. But this barrier too was safely passed.

In the troposphere the winds blew east, drifting the balloon and its rider far over the Sacramento ridges; in the higher stratosphere belt they blew westward again bringing him back over the White Sands Missile Range. One hour and a half after launch time, at almost precisely seven a.m., the balloon's pressure altimeter registered 103,300 feet (contradicting the radar altimeter at BCC ground control which showed 102,800 feet and was later accepted as the correct above-sea-level altitude). This was also float altitude, over the target area which had been pinpointed as a ten-mile-square plot on the range about 25 miles north of Holloman. At this altitude the balloon revolved slowly. The -36°F temperature allowed the heat to steam from the Jumper's mighty clothing bundle, wreathing him in light vapor. In spite of his plastic face visor the fierce sun glare was almost blinding. Something had happened to one of his pressure gloves, the hand ached with pain. He looked around and up and down at the hostile atmosphere and spoke into his recorder about it. All was blackness above, the white of cloud layers far below.

He prepared to jump.

The jump was neither a stunt nor for the purpose of establishing records. The fact that parachutes could not be used immediately at such heights because of opening shock, the problem of freezing or running out of oxygen during long slow descents, the matter of preventing a free-falling body from going into deadly spins, even the knowledge of physiological reactions and pressure-suit operation in low-pressure environments: such were the purposes that had started this aerospace research.

As far back as 1952 the science doctors at Wright-Patterson's Aero Medical Laboratory had begun. By 1954 dummy drops with parachutes were being tried. By 1957 higher dummy drops from balloons had entered the picture—and in 1959 a small multistage stabilizing chute created by Frances Beaupre to stop the 200-rpm spins that were "killing" the dummies (and certainly could kill a man) had started the real project rolling.

By that time it had been named Project Excelsior—which was interesting because Colonel John Paul Stapp himself did the naming (from the Latin meaning Ever Higher) and, as the new Aero Medical Laboratory chief, endorsed the program in full.

Live jumps from aircraft at lower altitudes had started the real tests, using several jumpers. Mostly veteran parachutists; for instance Captain Harry Collins, George Post with two hundred descents already under his ripcord and a Distinguished Flying Cross; Kittinger himself. In later tests at Holloman, Kittinger as project chief had made the first two balloon jumps, at altitudes near 75,000 feet. (In one the failure of the stabilizing-chute timer had almost spun him into eternity.)

Now the jump at better than 100,000 feet was the culminating leap.

Besides the new stabilizing chute, which would steady his fall until the main chute opened, the gondola with its equipment was another special creation. All its interior systems, command cutdown, communication, life-supporting, were Holloman creations devised specially for the project. Its twelve different camera setups (including one for National Geographic) had been cunningly rigged by Ken Arnold to catch every possible record of stress, angle, body attitude, other factors, during the ascent and the jump itself.

There was also the Jumper's Gargantua-producing personal equipment, the gear that was really under test and was to "bring him back alive."

Besides the special clothing and pressurized units one fundamental item was a kit containing a built-in oxygen system, a power device to de-ice his face mask, and accelerometers to measure body attitudes along all three axes. Strapped to his body was a tiny receiver-transmitter radio with its built-in aerial, a hook-blade survival knife fastened to a reserve parachute, and an emergency oxygen system attached to the same parachute. A more elaborate kit included a 14-channel tape recorder with separate channels for voice, heart beat, respiration, time blips, and skin and clothing temperatures.

A compact little package strapped to his wrist included an altimeter, stop watch, a second survival knife, and an outside mirror through which he could check his parachute canopy, usually an impossible job from within a pressure suit.

Not listed among the equipment but certainly a survival factor under the rough-and-ready exterior of a man who had "whipped jet planes around like bucking bronchos" was the rugged soul of the Jumper himself, who had already proved to be one of the coolest, calmest daredevils that ever donned an Air Force uniform.

At twelve minutes after seven he jumped.

Twenty seconds later the stabilizing chute opened; he was already down to 96,000 feet.

For four minutes and eighteen seconds he fell with the six-foot chute alone, through a thick cloud layer at 21,000 feet, down to 17,500 feet where the barometric aneroid opened his regular 28-foot parachute.

For 16½ miles he had fallen with an accumulating speed reaching 614 miles an hour at terminal velocity.

Thirteen minutes and forty-five seconds from the instant of leaving "the highest step in the world" he tumbled into the desert scrub almost at the center of the target area, where helicopters were already disgorging his aeromedical friends and technical and photo people.

His first words to them were: "I'm very glad to be back with you all."

"I'm very glad to be back with you all."

He said it with a grin to the assembled press and radio crowd in the BCC briefing room at ten o'clock that same morning—and the handclapping that had greeted his sudden entry was redoubled.

"Let me tell you about it first and then you can ask questions," he went on. "Or question my distinguished friends here." He indicated his supporting panel, Feldstein and Chubb, Beaupre, Billy Mills, BCC directors Markley and Major Irving Levin, the indispensable Gildenberg.

"We were able to do our first real high-altitude testing today with the Beaupre-designed stabilizing chute. Our whole team made this possible. I was the lucky one—I made the jump. But without all these ground people we couldn't have done it at all. We tested everything we could first, and then this human test was necessary. It showed us among other things that man's only limit is his imagination. My ascent today was completely normal. The gondola altimeter showed 103,300 feet. This has to be checked later. I blew all my ballast before reaching float altitude. Up there the sky looked dark enough to see stars as one would at night on earth. I had time, I looked, but there were no stars. The odd thing was that at float altitude the balloon turned and twisted slowly. I was up there after that about ten minutes. The sun was very brilliant. Another odd thing—there seemed to be a very thin cloud layer like cirrus, parallel to the balloon for thirty degrees to either side of the sun. And come to think of it, to the northwest at about 50,000 feet a tremendous black thunderstorm was gathering, simply tremendous. I'm going to ask my friend Duke Gildenberg here about these things. The countdown started at X-minus ninety seconds. At X-seventy I blew the antenna. That stopped all communication with the ground. When I stepped over I fell on my right side for about eight seconds, then on my back looking up at the balloon and that black sky for about ten seconds. After that the stabilizing chute opened—I looked up and saw it. There was absolutely perfect control during descent. At 21,000 feet I went into an overcast. I was still in it below 18,000 when the regular chute opened. From there on it was gravy—we proved our test and our mission. This was comparable to recovering a man from 103,000 feet—we placed a man in a space environment and protected him from low pressure, low temperatures, radiation. My free-fall time was about four minutes forty seconds. About ten minutes after that I was down."

He took a seat in the midst of new ripples of applause—a spontaneous and moving gesture from cynically hardened newsmen. The Associated Press man Harold Williams was there, Alamogordo Daily News editor Arylnn Bruer, KROD/TV's news chief Bruce Bissonette, KALG's tape-recording Terry Clark, and others now starting just as clamorous questions. But cigar-chewing Billy Mills had the floor.

"First let me quote these remarks Kit made at float altitude—I think they're significant. That's the first time we've ever had any man that high in an open basket with space he could reach out and touch. This is what he said through the comm system: 'There is a hostile sky above me. Man will never conquer space—he may live in it but he'll never conquer it. The sky above me is void and very hostile.'"

He sat down and Captain Feldstein was up the next instant. "I'd like to tell you this too before you all talk. At 50,000 feet Kittinger had some trouble with his right pressure glove. He didn't report this as he was afraid it would scrub everything. What it meant was that circulation was cut off in that hand exposing it practically to a vacuum. But as his flight surgeon it gave me a fit when he casually announced at float altitude: 'By the way, I'm not getting any pressure in my right hand.' I think that's something you should know too, the type of man he is."

The questions started up noisily and of every variety.

"Who did you talk to on first landing?"

"There was a foot race between Post, Chubb, and Fritz—I think it ended in a dead heat."

"Could you see the Grand Canyon?"

"Not with the overcast—but I could have seen it."

"Did you feel hot—cold—dizzy—any spinning?"

"Not hot, not cold, just right. And very little spinning."

"How did you feel at various altitudes?"

"Now that's an interesting question. Don't forget, I was a long time going up. There were three phases in this mission—first getting up, second getting out, third getting down. Actually, after all the time going up I was rather glad to jump."

"What clothing and equipment was removed right after touchdown?"

"First the pressure helmet. That's normal procedure. That's the most uncomfortable piece. Then everything down to shorts, for a complete change."

(He was in neat Air Force blues now.)

"What did you eat afterward, and when?"

"He hasn't eaten yet." (By Feldstein.)

"Did you call your wife yet?"

(By Mills.) "I placed a call right away at Wright Field and they notified Pauline—she knew fifteen minutes after touchdown."

"What about that license tag on the gondola?"

(The large freckled Kittinger grin appeared.) "If you want to know, my son thought his daddy needed a license plate there to do the job. So I just fastened it on. Incidentally the license plate is from Oregon, I'm from Florida, the project is from Ohio, we're doing this in New Mexico, so you see even without space trips we do get around." (General laughter.)

"What could you see from float altitude?"

"I could see El Paso. And Guadaloupe in the distance. This was during the ninety-degree turns in descending."

"What about that hand camera you took up?"

"It froze about 15,000 feet."

"Did the gondola come down all right?"

"Twenty-seven miles due west of Tularosa—on its way back here now."

"What kind of helmet did you wear?"

"A standard Air Force M-3 partial pressure helmet."

The clamor continued. And then as it wore away to an extent the Jumper stood up and the large freckled grin came with a final statement.

"Now if there's no more at this time I'll go call my wife."

By the time the newsmen had flashed their stories across the nation the deluge had started in the little Holloman information office; telephones and telegrams wanting more information, facts, details, more facts—and Kittinger himself.

The London Daily Mail wanted to know how terminal velocity had been calculated. The Columbia Broadcasting System wanted details for a network broadcast. The El Paso and Albuquerque news agencies wanted pictures rushed express collect. Radio stations from Texas, Oklahoma, Colorado, California wanted taped stories, preferably from Kittinger himself again. TV agencies telephoned about national coverage. Local radio stations wanted to make personal visits.

By early afternoon LIFE Magazine's New Mexico staffer Arch Napier was on a chartered plane for a special interview with the man who had created this magnificent turmoil.

The interview took place that same day in the information office, at this writer's desk, where the 32-year-old Jumper, now in flying clothes again after a quick trip to his own Wright-Patterson headquarters, still red-headed and ruddy-faced, looking like anything but a poet's idea of an idealist, indicated just what he thought of fame and how much of an idealist he really was.

Napier, who was also a sensitive individual (and a warm and trusted friend in the information office, never betraying a deadline) delicately felt his way through the possibilities of an exclusive story.

Kittinger's answer was a simple one.

"I couldn't have done the job alone, without the Holloman crew, the Dayton crew, the Cambridge people—and Colonel John Paul Stapp who planned out the whole idea. So any story at all has just as much to do with them, it just splits all ways."

On the basis of that mutual understanding he gave the rest of his interview—not as an "exclusive" by Kittinger but still as a man saying what he himself believed in. At the end he was still trying to sum it up by saying:

" . . . Because this project was no stunt, you see. And never meant to be. Sometimes the news gets it wrong, or builds it wrong, but I want you to understand, this was done for scientific knowledge and nothing else. We've got to know these things to be able to get our pilots down again when something goes wrong. We've got to know all about those hazards up there, out in space. No one man can do much of it. And no one man anywhere in the picture can stand out alone."

So in the end Captain Joseph Kittinger of the United States Air Force had made his point—for himself and the United States Air Force.

8

SPACE ANIMALS

Chimpanzee Into Chimponaut

USUALLY IN THINKING OF DOCTORS one is reminded of hospitals, crowded waiting rooms full of sad-eyed patients, the portly man with the bedside manner thumping brother Willie's scrawny chest while Willie murmurs "Ahhhh!" In short the traditional picture. But at Holloman there was a group of doctors who had departed from this tradition.

True, there was another group, practicing medicos, to be seen any day moving through the long quiet hallways or in the many rooms of Holloman's regular hospital, going about their professional duties. The first group, however, seldom saw the inside of a hospital (unless sick themselves) and certainly had no waiting rooms full of patients. Medical doctors, flight surgeons, veterinarians, pathologists, X-ray specialists, biologists, psychologists, they lived a quite different workaday existence, collected in an assortment of buildings in Holloman's North Area where the high red Aerobee tower could be seen a mile off to one side and the busy drone squadron hangars on another.

In short, they were research scientists. They were also a part of the Aeromedical Field Laboratory, later called the Aeromedical Research Laboratory—and in departing one medical tradition they had only been helping to build another. What they were concerned with was the medical science of the future as it related to all known and unknown problems in man's effort to conquer space.

From its modest beginnings as a mere annex to larger Air Force research centers the Laboratory had grown in many directions, not the least being in size and professional significance. During those earlier days it had launched the first living creatures into notably high altitudes—mice and monkeys as high as 36 miles in Aerobee rockets, somewhat lower in V-2 rockets and balloons—and laid some of the groundwork for its later purely original studies. It launched John Paul Stapp on his famous rocket-sled windblast rides and other men in the Manhigh gondola flights to the 20-mile edge of space. By degrees its main lines of research had fallen into two broad fields, space biology and biodynamics; centered on the human hazards that had to be overcome in each. And so the busy "science doctors" without waiting rooms and patients had stayed busy, adding some totally new facts to the knowledge of life-support systems, escape systems, B-52 harnesses, ejection seat capsules, biomedical adequacies in space vehicles, acceleration and reentry stresses, high G forces and weightlessness, cosmic radiation dangers, temperature and humidity variables, low pressure and low oxygen effects, underwater subgravity reactions, the results of other unusual environments on both animal and man.

For both animal and man had become involved—as inevitable a process as history has always shown it to be. With the use of animals the doctors and their talented assistants had found they were working closer to the answers to a good many of their problems. Thus as the Laboratory's human population had grown so had its animal population, at times to as many as 400 clinically observed creatures representing as many as nine species. (The largest numbers being mice, a conveniently small biological unit.) Most of them seemed to thrive with the unusual care they got, and were both useful and continuing subjects.

And then as always happens there was one species that turned out to be the outstanding subject—the most useful, and easily the most gifted. This was the chimpanzee.

Presently the Lab had acquired more than fifty of them.

About the same number of people were there and one of them was Jim Cook.

Jim was a big, soft-spoken, rather seriously disposed man though with frequent glints of humor in his mild slate-blue eyes, young-middle-aged, hardly ever given to visible displays of anger—and if there was one thing clearer than another about him it was that he loved animals. As a matter of fact he was just as friendly toward his fellowman.

There was a place called the Vivarium which was a part of the Laboratory and it was full of animals. Jim Cook was in charge of them. When I first met him he was an Air Force captain (later a major), but he was a doctor too, a veterinarian, as well as the Lab's chief pathologist. His life work had been animals. And above all he seemed fond of the chimps. He could talk about them for hours.

"We get most of our little fellows from the Cameroons in equatorial Africa. In fact they're classified as an anthropoid ape of Africa—in the Latin known as *Pan satyrus*, sometimes as *Pan troglodyte*—a primitive little man not too unlike ourselves."

His blue eyes twinkled for no reason at all.

"Usually we try to get them as babies, one to three years of age. If we can examine them on the spot it's by weight and teeth. At one year they should have all their temporary teeth and weigh twelve to fifteen pounds. But in the wild state they're often stunted in growth too, so we certainly have to watch that.

"After they reach Holloman we segregate them for about six weeks and build them up to gain confidence. Also to give them full physical checkups and eliminate parasites and disease carriers. It's sort of quarantine—as soon as it's over they're allowed to join our regular colony and in about six months we can use them with other chimps in the space biology programs."

With no prompting at all he went right on.

"From the beginning we feed them a balanced diet of fresh fruit, pablum, gelatin, condensed milk, a health cocktail, a chimp cracker like a Graham cracker—and plenty of vitamins. We also use common pediatric medicines and antibiotics and the usual oral preparations. Not that we've found anything 'usual'—no textbook knowledge—we've just had to learn as we go. A matter of teaching each other." Again his eyes twinkled. "The whole idea is to produce a normal healthy animal so we can get accurate baseline data and compare that with human data.

"We've also found they have ordinary human ailments, just like children. For instance dental troubles—we might have to extract a tooth. Now we hang rubber tires in their cages to be used as teething rings. They're subject to measles, whooping-cough, malaria—and the only animal we know of that gets the common human cold. We give them gamma globulin to help against such conditions, also tuberculin tests, and frequent clinical checkups for blood pressure, temperature, pulse and respiration rates, progressive weight, ear-nose-throat complaints. In fact with our scientific diets and handling, these little fellows grow faster and healthier than in their native jungles and certainly have longer life spans."

Like a man warming to his work he went into further medical details.

"During their activity hours we know the percentage of carbohydrates, fats, proteins, and starches in each chimp intake. In that way we regulate his diet to get him to work. As an example we might cut the caloric intake from fifteen hundred to a thousand calories a day. We also feed him eighteen percent protein diet—it's a mistaken conception that all chimps are vegetarians. Another thing we've found is that they have the common A and O blood factors and we're learning to match these types for blood transfusions. Unless it's for medical care we never use anaesthetics in cage handling. But we do follow the American Medical Association rules in all our animal handling and I wouldn't have it any other way—we're stricter with our handlers than with our chimps. Though as a matter of fact they get so fond of each other that it's no problem."

As if that last thought released the deepest springs in his nature he leaned back from his untidy desk, picked up some of the glossy 8 x 10 photos we had been looking at, and smiled over them less like a doctor than a benevolent friend.

"They're really the most sociable creatures, you know. At first they're shy, but they get over that. Once in a while some new little fellow fails to respond and then we try to find him a companion so he can really hobnob. They seem to have as many individual traits as we do—some are congenial, some nasty, some alert, some lazy, some just contrary. We have a few who even bully their fellows—those we call the Hitlers. On the other hand one of our friendliest females, Minnie, mothered a baby male when he got here—fussed over him, cuddled him, taught him how to eat. Mostly they're great extroverts and show-offs. They like to play tug-of-war in groups and they're full of mischief. Their sense of humor seems very definite—they enjoy a joke and grin over it. They'll squirt each other with a water hose—one day young Rocky got the hose away from a cage handler and had a rare time squirting the man until he could be caught again. Also they're great mimics and imitators. They play with their space jackets, take a jacket off and try it on their fellows. If one sees an attendant peeling an orange, the next time he'll peel it too. Their food preferences are very definite. They love lemon drops, coca cola, banana stalks. They'll hold a coke bottle as expertly as a human. And they eat more daintily than some humans. We suspect that's why they're free of many parasitic diseases contracted by other animals. Undoubtedly they have the power of reasoning. They'll try to open doors and untie shoe laces. A chimp will use a stick like a tool to get an apple out from under something. He'll think out which rope to pull on to get food. He'll also call over his fellows and they'll 'discuss' the problem. They recognize symbolic values, colors, poker chips— they'll accept poker chips as rewards and exchange them later for some delicacy. So far our advanced students like Ham, Enos, Duane, Paleface, Bobby Joe, Chang, Elvis, Tiger, Roscoe, Little Jim, Minnie, Chu can recognize as many as five different selection symbols—and the best ones seem to work for the sheer joy of working. Of course they're much higher on the phylogenetic scale than any other primate except man, in fact the nearest thing to human that an animal can be basically and temperamentally. That's why they're the outstanding animal for our space biology studies here, which call for 'human' responses to space-simulated conditions."

He paused there. For a moment he seemed talked out. But such a grand and natural flow of facts not only ticketed the man (one full of human kindliness, professional integrity, genuine interest in what he was doing, most eminently the right man in the right job) but magnificently uncovered brand new avenues to explore.

For instance the matter of that health cocktail, the weird assortment of personal names, more about space jackets—and certainly more about space biology programs.

"But one subject at a time!" He held a hand up and chuckled. "The health cocktail is our own concoction, a high-protein mixture of pablum, jello, whipped eggs and milk, very pink when it comes out— somebody once called it a soda-jerker's dream. But the chimps love it. As for the way they get their names, that's strictly haphazard. Mostly from their handlers—but what really counts is the numbered brass tag around each one's neck, just like a soldier's dog tag. That's the number they're registered by in their clinical records, and a positive identity. Then about the space jackets. Another misnomer. They're made of nylon web-mesh, something like a long-legged, one-piece bathing suit, laced in the back, and their only use is to hold various sensors in place which busy little chimp fingers would otherwise pick at—devices for recording physiological responses, pulse and respiration rates, temperature, EKG readings, matters we have to know about while the animal is working."

"And the space biology programs?"

"Wouldn't it be better to see for yourself?"

I had been drooling over the possibility.

The three long low Vivarium buildings, arranged in a sort of unfinished quadrangle within a large steel-fenced plot of the usual bare desert, were fairly cluttered with outside cages and wire-enclosed runs where dozens of chimpanzee space candidates were disporting themselves with all allowable freedom. Inside were more cages, long corridors, any number of rooms equipped for the care and handling and training preparations that were creating another bedlam of activity all through the compound.

There was a clinical room, a hospital room, an X-ray room, a laboratory section full of appurtenances for the usual biochemistry or pathology tasks such as tissue study, blood and urine analysis, parasitology work, there were holding-areas where animals played in groups and dressing areas where they were being rounded up one after another to be fitted into their space suits with all the accompanying uproar and romping of a crowd of unruly children.

They were by no means a silent animal. The throaty low *huf-huf-huf-huf-huf-huf-huf-huf-huf-huf* that got louder and louder culminating in a wild sustained shriek like a diva holding a high C was to become a most familiar sound, but when first heard it was actually alarming. On the other hand the noisiest might be climbing all over their handlers snuggling as affectionately as babies demanding the ultimate in security. And when one knee-high youngster tugged at my own pants-leg and then put a hand in mine, watching me quietly as if there were no point in ever letting hands go—one more chimpanzee convert had been made on the spot.

The handlers were of various ranks, commissioned and enlisted, military and civilian, veterinary officers and animal attendants; most of them in white medical coats that again made the operation uniquely different from the usual military scene. A dark-haired captain, Jerry Fineg—said to be one of the best animal handlers in the business—was in charge here.

Except for female chimps not a woman was in the place.

And though it seemed rough and rowdy there was order. On clinical tables the otoscope and opthalmascope prying went on, sphygmomanometer bands were wrapped in place for blood pressure readings, thermometers and stethoscopes were in evidence to detect other conditions. Meekly the subjects sat as if aware of such benefits for their own well-being. (Or perhaps it was the Fineg efficiency—with his wry grin he seemed to have them all under control.)

There was more behavior variety in the dressing rooms. Yammering and screeching and jumping, cuffing amongst some, soothing words from attendants, an occasional candy tidbit or food pellet brought out of a pocket and seized greedily.

And presently the wire-trailing, heart-activity sensors, the electrodes, the rectal temperature probes were taped in place and the space suits fitted.

Before the chimp colony had been established the other animals making the Vivarium their home had included a few bears, some pigs, cats and dogs, fish, frogs, rats and mice—one fabulous strain of California black mice with a record of generations of pure breeding important to many kinds of biological research. But unquestionably the chimps had stolen the entire show, creating a three-ring circus for themselves and their handlers that went on endlessly, day after day.

Only with the space suits in place and the ride in panel trucks to the training building a mile away came the real significance of the "circus."

I shall not soon forget my first sight of chimpanzees in training. Four of them sat in their space chambers closely adjoining one another and their names, as I heard presently from the white-coated lieutenant in charge, were Minnie, Tiger, Elvis, and Chang. They were among the youngsters of the colony. All four had the same rounded little bellies, flap ears, liquid-brown eyes and old-man faces showing patiently resigned expressions as they leaned back in their small metal chairs yawning and dozing between training stints, fingering their instrument handles, pulling absently at their belts, seemingly ignoring the world.

But the world was not ignoring them. Especially the people involved in the world's greatest venture to date—that of exploring other worlds. Like the seven human astronauts being trained at that time for the nation's first manned orbital project, here too sat some of its potential candidates—and Destiny, like an invisible sign, most certainly hovered over their broad troglodyte brows.

"Restraint Conditioning of Large Biological Specimens" had been the name of the first tentative project—soon to branch into a variety of more sophisticated programs. Perhaps the chimpanzee idea had started with Rufe Hessberg—doctor, flight surgeon, School of Aviation Medicine graduate and lieutenant colonel, who was in charge of the Laboratory. At least some of the people there were giving him credit for it. With the lieutenant, William Ward, from the Lab's Ecology section, Captain Dan Mosely from the Biodynamics section, Captain Grover Schock who had the distinction of being the first Ph.D. scientist in space physiology (earning his degree at the University of Illinois), the lively minded Hessberg had worked out the training details from theories based on the many ways in which physically, metabolically, and temperamentally, *Pan troglodyte* and *Homo sapiens* seemed more like Big and Little cousins than man and anthropoid on the variegated primate scale.

The purposes of the Restraint Conditioning project had been laid down as fourfold: (1) to study the psycho-physiology of young chimpanzees under altered environmental conditions, (2) to test the restraint conditioning possibilities within isolated environments, (3) to teach the subjects a series of conditioned responses under such effects, and (4) to orient the subjects to conditions of actual flight.

To *study*, to *test*, to *teach*, to *orient*—these were the action words out of which the programs were being fashioned to answer the biomedical question marks such as just how *Pan* (and man himself) might react to outer-space conditions, restraint, isolation, weightlessness, acceleration, deceleration, physical and mental requirements, and actual flight.

It was all an aeromedical idea and it had started at Holloman.

The restraint chair was an inhouse-designed sheet metal structure built to chimp size, low on the ground, upholstered with insolite, holed in the seat and potted underneath for natural evacuation uses, with slotted nylon straps buckling behind to hold the subject in a normal sitting position while operating his psychomotor levers or undergoing some related training phase.

The psychomotor device was one of the absolute keys to the training situation—operator's panel, instrument panel, flight control panel all in one. Actually there were several kinds, generally in the form of metal boxes about the size of a small suitcase, electronically activated to throw varicolored lights or lighted symbols on the small square screen openings at the front of the panel. Under the light screens, long lever handles were affixed for easy grasping by the animal as he was put through simple and then more complicated jobs of levering the lights off in given time periods, watching to respond to random lights, and learning by the reward-and-punishment principle of receiving very slight and completely harmless electric shocks through his plated gym shoes or, for work well done, banana-flavored food pellets and copious squirts of water through automatic dispensing devices likewise rigged into the equipment.

The "space chambers" in use were also of various kinds, some inhouse-built and some manufactured. Basically they were all for the purpose of conducting prolonged ground tests under a variety of space-simulated conditions including isolation, temperature, humidity, and pressure. Behind them stood the instrumented program racks which controlled the chamber conditions and psychomotor tasks: high metal frameworks full of exposed wiring, relays, timers, switches, looking for all the world like half-finished telephone switchboards.

"But they're smarter than telephones," the lieutenant said. "All we do is crank in the programs and they do the work."

Or as he explained more thoroughly, each rack was designed to perform the following: (1) present stimuli to the animal by means of timed lights or other signals directing his work requirements, (2) present positive or negative reinforcements, in other words rewards or punishments, (3) record all results of programmed tests digitally, by numerical counters, and (4) record the same results electronically on magnetic tape.

The results were then analyzed and the work of training, by more and more refined tasks and by the psychological process known as transfer of learning, went on.

"With this equipment and our sled runs and a good many C-131 flights," said the attentive young lieutenant, who had majored in biology and seemed as dedicated to the entire space program as any astronaut ready for orbit, "each of our chimps in turn gets used to conditions like sudden noise, vibration, G forces, weightlessness, unusual temperatures and humidity—and I think I'm safe in saying that before man flies out into space and comes back alive one of our chimps will have to do it first."

But neither Lieutenant Ward nor his listener even dreamed at that moment how prophetic his words really were. Nor for that matter did the four talented chimps (if they could have known such things) as they still sat in their restraint chairs alternately working and relaxing, banging their levers with unbelievable rapidity as the flashing blue and white and red lights came on, making very few misses by this time, sucking their water pipes and reaching for their food pellets with all the nonchalance of skilled craftsmen knowing exactly what they were doing, once in a while letting out a wild *huf-huf-huf-huf-huf-huf-huf* or ear-piercing scream as if from sheer high spirits—and again yawning or scratching or apparently dozing and ignoring the world.

Later in their careers they would be engaged in far more intricate psychomotor tasks such as oddity problems, symbol selection, delayed responses, multi-time sequences, tracking operations consisting of aligning pairs of punched lights—advancing from "high school" to "college" and then post-graduate courses on their way to becoming full-fledged space candidates.

But all these matters were of the future, too. And only gradually would the crystal ball become clear, sharpening its images until the ball itself might seem like the orbiting space capsule.

For these four chimps were Minnie, Tiger, Elvis, and Chang. Numbers 46, 47, 35, and 65. The destiny of three of them some time in that future would be to journey to a place called Cape Canaveral.

And the destiny of one of the three—Number 65, whose name would change from Chang to HAM—would be a longer journey, as the first chimpanzee rocketed into space.

9

SPACE AGE TRACK

The World's Most Unusual Railroad

THE SMALL BLUE CARRYALL TRUCK moved rapidly along the concrete apron beside the two shining steel ribbons of track. But not so rapidly that it had to heed the large conspicuous warning sign ahead.

MAXIMUM SPEED LIMIT 3,000 MILES AN HOUR!

"That's Mach four," said the blue-uniformed officer in the carryall. "Originally the sign was meant for a joke but I'm afraid it has to go. We're so close to Mach four now that after a sled run last week we found a dead coyote, a dead skunk, and a bird right between the tracks. Near the water brake troughs. They must have come to drink and simply couldn't get out of the way."

The chatty officer was Lieutenant Colonel Donald Vlcek, chief of the test track division. The carryall was a piece of division property. Driving it was a young lieutenant, Pete Mullins, fresh out of engineering college but already one of the track's experienced project officers. We were on our way to a track run now.

"So a speed cop would have to go four times as fast as sound to catch up with any violators?" I suggested lightly.

"They might call him a space cop." The colonel looked just as amused.

The lieutenant, looking like some kind of spaceman himself in his blue-and-gold striped safety helmet, presently halted the carryall. At the side of the track half a dozen men were crouched in a huddle working over a small steel cylinder about the size and shape of a thermos bottle. Some wore red helmets, some yellow. I had learned that the blue-and-gold marked the lieutenant as today's project officer. Red meant the rocket propulsion crew. Yellow meant the instrumentation crew. The colonel wore a helmet too—plain white, the color for the track's supervisory personnel.

As an official visitor my own helmet was a bright green.

Within the shiny steel cylinder nestled the test item for the morning's run, a magnetic tape recorder intended for missile telemetry. On the track stood the sled. Or rather on half the track, for it was a monorail sled, the size of a carpenter's long tool box, but built of tough thick steel, nosed like a pie-wedge for streamlining, fitted to the rail with fore-and-aft U-shaped steel slippers, the contrivances that held the sled on the track. Behind it extended a flange, fitted underneath with another slipper, to hold the booster rockets in place. The rockets, four for today's firing, thin and tubular, about five feet long, tied together like a bundle of fasces, rested on the concrete apron near the sled.

In both directions stretched the track, two 4½- by 6-inch rails seven miles long, seven feet apart, anchored to the heavy concrete by thousands of powerful tie-bolts, to furnish a roadbed of such precision that irregularities over five-thousandths of an inch were smoothed down with oxyacetylene torches and grinding tools. Truly a Space Age railroad—the longest, most carefully engineered, most elaborately instrumented test track in the world.

"At a cost of some twelve million dollars so far," the colonel said, casually lowering the short black pipe he was smoking. "The rails came from the Bethlehem Steel Company in Pennsylvania. In thirty-nine-foot sections, numbered so they could be joined in the same order. After laying them out here each rail was forge-welded into one continuous length right on the spot. To make them absolutely straight they had to be pulled out like rubber bands so to speak, with hydraulic jacks, to create zero tension at 120 degrees Fahrenheit. All the work was done at night so the precision tools wouldn't be affected by daily heat changes."

The heat was there as we talked. All the region around us was baked almost every day of the year by fierce sunshine. In rolling uneven patches the desert stretched off on both sides, bordered on the west by the glistening odd gypsum line of White Sands—now perfectly mirage-like in having transformed itself into a vast and shimmering lake. (How many times in future that illusory sight would beckon!)

In the near distance, along the seven miles of track construction, extended the complex of small hardly visible facilities I had heard described as its nervous system. Blockhouses, pillboxes, firing stations, booster buildings, a missile assembly building. A thousand feet to the east of its north-south line were the concrete camera pads, on a parallel line at every 500 feet, the "eyes" of the track, 72 pads in all. Also 12 high camera tracking towers for long-focal-length work or end-to-end panning.

A short way behind the camera pads stood the Midway Building, which I had also visited with the genial colonel that morning. More technically known as the telemetry building, pulsing center of the entire network, connected by ground wires, coaxial cables, radio links—full of telemetry, banks of tape recorders, timers, programmers, data reduction readers. Green-tinted oscilloscope windows had stared at me like so many Cyclops' eyes. The speedometer-like windows of the timers had visibly ticked off the seconds in an electronic countdown, changing the figures to red as they moved toward firing time.

"That's the building known as the brains of the track," the colonel had said. "Where every sled run is recorded and analyzed."

But as we stood on the track apron now, it turned out that firing time was being delayed. The lieutenant, in his blue-and-gold helmet, had joined the men in red and yellow helmets and was listening as they explained the trouble.

"Darn recorder just took off and ran out all its tape."

Actually it was minor trouble. And presently the crews were fixing it. Working near their own well-equipped truck. Still others were wiring the sled itself. Today's run was called an environmental sled run. To test the specially modified tape recorder which had been instrumented with accelerometers and other devices to furnish the Midway "brain" such information as rates of physical temperature under stress, rates of pressure, flutter or vibration, acceleration or velocity changes, several other measurements.

Transducers on the sled turned the physical stresses into electrical signals. Midway telemetry receivers intercepted the signals. Data recorders allowed quick-look readings before computer reduction furnished complete analyses which in turn led to new improvements in the test instrument itself.

The four rockets being used to power the sled were of the Loki type. Loaded weight 17.8 pounds. Burning time 0.78 seconds. Thrust about 3,000 pounds. Velocity 2,700 feet per second—comparatively "slow," only about two and a half times the speed of sound!

Now the trouble with the recorder had been corrected; the lieutenant politely offered us precedence, climbed back into the blue carryall. The next moment we were driving off the concrete apron, out across the weed-clumped desert itself. But not far. A hundred yards away stood the concrete pillbox, about five feet high, a shell wide enough for half a dozen persons. Joltingly the carryall rolled behind it. Other vehicles were already there. A noisy large carrier-generator juiced the portable two-way radio set which had ben placed with its low antenna on top of the pillbox for communication with the entire track area. Beside it stood a small intercom box from which wires trailed along the ground back to the track. A man in a white helmet was speaking through it to the men at the track.

"Move your truck—the sled must be seen from here at all times."

The colonel made the new introductions. The man in the white helmet like his own turned out to be Major Dawson, the fire control officer; responsible for both the countdown and the actual firing. Genially acknowledging the introduction he watched the large round face of the chronometer-type clock near his fire control box. Its second hand swept around and around.

He waved his free hand to one of the propulsion crew in a nearby vehicle. Suddenly a red flare shot high in the air, trailing a ribbon of smoky flame on its way down.

"Attention on the net . . . X minus fifteen minutes on the monorail sled, repeat, fifteen minutes . . . mark!"

Closely watching his clock, he continued the countdown.

"X minus fourteen minutes—"

"X minus thirteen—"

He watched the clock and the men on the track, who were busy with the rocket bundle now. He also talked with the colonel.

"Explain our firing system," suggested the colonel, using his pipe to gesture amiably. "Don't forget its foolproof features."

(The colonel must have known every detail himself—but perhaps he believed in tossing the ball around.)

"It's this way," said the major. "You see that unit over there—" he pointed to a small wheeled cart near the track, at this distance resembling a white ice cream wagon. "That's our portable power supply for the firing circuit. Maybe you can see the little green panel at one side—try these binoculars a second. When the panel is inserted the circuit is open—the rockets can't be fired even accidentally from here."

"Nor anywhere else," murmured the colonel.

"The circuit is also kept open by this key and its separate toggle switch," the major went on. He indicated them on his fire control panel, which also stood on the pillbox. "The sled is fired electrically—they wire the rockets for that. When it's armed the first circuit out there is closed—"

He interrupted himself for the countdown. "X minus seven minutes on the monorail . . . mark!"

He went on. "When that first circuit is closed the firing can only be done from here. And only by this key and toggle switch. Furthermore no other key will fit—and there are no duplicates. At X minus thirty seconds I turn the key—that closes the second circuit. At zero I push the toggle switch—"

He interrupted himself again. "X minus six minutes on the monorail run." Watching the clock for exact timing he added: "Mark!"

He watched the track. The men there had finished installing the rockets. One moved to the small power supply cart. His voice came back to the pillbox through the intercom set.

"Are we clear to arm the sled?"

Instead of answering the major pressed a button opening a channel on his radio set and spoke into his hand microphone.

"Are we clear to arm the sled?"

In an aside the colonel remarked: "He's talking with the safety officer who's moving somewhere in the track area."

An answer must have come presently through the major's headset. He pressed another button and spoke into the intercom set.

"You are clear to arm the sled."

The men at the track became busy again—wiring the rockets now. The major went on with his countdown.

"X minus five minutes on the monorail run—"

The men at the track moved back to the power supply cart, removed the small green panel, inserted a red one. "They've wired the rockets," said the lieutenant. The next moment the men piled into their truck and began driving off the concrete apron. The major opened his radio channels and spoke into his microphone.

"The sled is now armed."

It turned out that he was alerting the local area, the Midway building, the safety officer, everyone else in the track area. Going on to explain, he added: "The circuit's closed now up to the fire control point. Everything else will proceed from here."

All the men at the track had gotten into the truck and now it was rolling bumpily across the mesquite toward the pillbox.

"X minus four minutes on the monorail run . . . mark!"

The truck and its riders arrived at the pillbox.

"All armed?" asked the major.

"All armed," came the answer.

The slender black hand of the clock swept around and around.

"X minus three minutes—"

The tiny sled with its live rocket bundle looked small and isolated on the track—and utterly harmless.

"Did one ever explode?" I wanted to know.

"A few," remarked the colonel. "Out of hundreds fired. Sometimes they still push the sled and we don't know. That is, until we reach the sled later."

"X minus two minutes—"

The people behind the pillbox huddled more closely. The clock hand swept around and around.

"X minus one minute on the monorail sled run . . . mark!"

A red flare shot into the air again. The countdown went on in seconds.

"Fifty-five . . . fifty . . . forty-five . . ."

At X minus thirty seconds the major turned the key in his fire control box.

"Now he can fire only by the toggle switch," said the colonel.

"Twenty-seven . . . twenty-six . . . twenty-five . . ."

Everyone behind the pillbox peered carefully from the sides.

"Look a bit ahead along the track if you want to see anything," said the lieutenant helpfully.

The clock hand went around and around. The major counted.

". . . four . . . three . . . two . . . FIRE!"

He pushed his switch.

An immense flash of red-orange flame. A thunderous rolling roar like a thousand Bunsen burners. The flash a streak, the streak miles long. Over.

I found myself still peering. "So that's it! How far did it go?"

"Twenty thousand feet. From firing point to track end," said the colonel.

The lieutenant waited for us to climb into the carryall again, then got in himself. The next moment we were rolling back toward the concrete apron. The instant had come and gone so completely that the effect still was closer to stunned bewilderment.

"It's always that way," said the lieutenant, grinning a bit. "All the buildup, then whoooooosh!"

"The buildup, and the aftermath," said the colonel. "Hyphenated by that all-important flash."

The carryall came rapidly on to the concrete apron once more, following the vanished flash. Within a few moments the end of the track was reached—with only the desert itself beyond. The crews in red and yellow helmets were already there. Also other people, who had come from the nearby blockhouse—Blockhouse Coco at the north end of the track. Also the sled, which the crews were dismantling now. Tangled around the sled and its empty boosters were dozens of white and shredded streamers, polyethylene plastic, still wet and dripping—the obvious cause of the water now splashed everywhere in the track vicinity.

"Our latest monorail braking system," said the colonel, climbing down from the carryall. "We're proud of it," he added, "for it was our own idea. It works fine. Simple, too. Just water bags. Like sausages, laid along the track. It's too bad you couldn't have seen the splashing!"

The safety officer, who was there too, had been completing his survey for the All Clear signal. Now he called out to one of the propulsion crew.

"Your gun ready, Sergeant?"

The sergeant drew out his stumpy weapon, a Very pistol, Army Ordnance signal type. (One item that had needed no modernizing since World War I.)

With a report like a loud firecracker the last flare of the run, a green one this time, arched as gracefully as its predecessors into the air.

"I must tell you more about the track and the instrumentation itself," said the colonel as we sipped our coffee in his office, where several generous-sized windows offered a clean sweep of the area he commanded.

On the walls were half a dozen framed and matted color prints in large size, vivid images of various rocket sleds in action: a black-and-white striped Pershing impact sled resembling nothing so much as a gigantic rifle bullet; an Aerojet liquid-engine with its three immense thrust chambers spitting out smoke and special rocket fuel; a prototype of the Snark missile, wings and tail-spread and all, sled-borne instead of airborne, one of the earliest test projects, when the track itself had been only a fraction of its present length.

"For instance it's interesting to know how straight the track is." He carefully restuffed his pipe. "I can tell you it's so exact that its minimum curvature-radius equals a million lineal feet—over one-tenth that of the earth. In other words the track is straighter than the horizon itself."

"Why does it have to be?"

"Another form of test precision. For profiling each run with maximum accuracy. For reducing G forces generated through centrifugal effect."

I was interested in the matter of "rails pulled out like rubber bands" and said as much.

"But that's what I'm talking about—alignment!" He grinned broadly through a cloud of smoke. "If you've ridden a fast train over a rough rail bed you must know what vibration is. So imagine a light sled whizzing along at three thousand miles an hour! What we're actually trying to duplicate is free missile flight. So we've had to eliminate the pounding. First we built the concrete foundation—like a U-shaped beam to anchor the rails. The concrete can stand 70,000 pounds of vertical download, 25,000 pounds of upload, more than 40,000 pounds of lateral loading. It also takes sled weights up to 20,000 pounds on each slipper. Then we stretched the two 35,000-foot rails—or 35,071 feet to be exact—and gained another twenty-three and a half feet."

"You mean you stretched *steel*?"

"Precisely." (It was plain that he enjoyed my amazement.) "The 39-foot factory lengths were forge-welded into single 10,000-foot lengths. Also a pair of 5,000-foot lengths. Then each of these was anchored down at one end while hydraulic jacks pulled at the other. When they had the length that proved tension-free for 120-degree temperatures each of the two rails was welded into one continuous length and tied down to the concrete every fifty-two inches. By stretching we did away with heat buckling as well as thrust distortions."

I sipped my coffee and thought it over.

"Also there's the stopping problem," the colonel went on. "Especially for the faster heavier sleds. For the monorails we use parachutes or drag flaps or the polyethylene bags you saw this morning. Actually it's easier with the dual-rail sleds. You must have noticed the water troughs between the rails—a bit over a foot deep. At eleven-foot intervals breakable dams keep the troughs full and scoops under the sleds catch the water and transfer momentum away from the sleds. We can also vary the water volume to program exact velocity and deceleration changes."

"How do you measure velocity?"

"Mainly by light beams. Photo-sensing devices. At thirteen-foot intervals track interrupters break the beam from a sensing-head on the sled as it goes by. The head directs this collimated beam onto the photo-sensing device. The pulses in microvolts are radioed to the Midway building. There they trigger a digitizer which reads out the velocities in microseconds and codes the record on tape."

How much there was to know—and how much the colonel did know! I was full of respect. But of course there was even more.

"I might mention a minor point about all this data acquisition—not really impressive but the kind of point you writers like." Mildly he waved his pipe and chuckled. "To build such a network we've put enough ground lines and coaxial cables in the track system to reach from here to Moscow."

"In a single line?"

"Of course. There's another statistic someone thought up—and you may have noticed I'm fond of statistics. Enough steel has gone into the track to build twenty-five hundred Cadillacs."

"That must have been a news report too."

"As a matter of fact we think up a lot of them ourselves. For instance there's enough concrete in the track system to build a three-foot sidewalk two hundred miles long. And enough dirt was moved—this beautiful desert dirt—to bury one of our Western ghost towns. If it ever needed burying." He grinned again. "But I've been waiting for you to ask the sixty-four dollar question."

"What question is that?"

"Why do we use a high-speed test track?"

"To test missiles?"

"Basically true. But it can be broken down more interestingly. There are other test tracks, you know—in California the one at Edwards Air Force Base, the Navy's China Lake track—at Hurricane Mesa in Utah one pointing off a cliff, mostly for seat-ejection tests. But ours is the longest, actually the last word in test tracks, and likely to be for some time. For instance we can simulate a flight with a guidance system and collect all the data from blastoff to reentry conditions. In fact by comparing the position computed by the guidance system with the known position of the sled, it's possible to determine the accuracy of the guidance system itself. We also do impact testing of warheads, flutter testing of airfoil sections, acceleration-deceleration-vibration tests on all kinds of instrumentation, aeromedical studies for windblast and G loading, reentry studies of nose cones, ballistic profiles, rain erosion tests, anthropomorphic dummy runs and seat ejection tests, chimpanzee runs—and sometimes we've run human volunteers and made *that* our payload."

"Any other kinds?"

"Those and more. Each with its own special angles, of course."

My writing fingers itched.

"Furthermore there's the one big advantage in almost all our tests— at the other end of the track our engineers recover the test object and find out what, if anything, went wrong. In fact that's how the Holloman track got its name—the captive missile test track."

"Is there one like it in Russia?"

"If there is they've kept it a better secret than Sputnik."

There was an interruption—a pretty secretary with a pretty hairdo stuck her head in the doorway and murmured: "Buzzer on three-seven, Colonel Vlcek."

With the phone in hand he lingered another few seconds, still smiling. "Have I told you what you want to know?"

"More than I knew there was to know."

"Wait till we show you our supersonic ball game—catching a flying artillery shell with a rocket sled. You haven't seen anything yet!"

But as I went away it was hard to decide which to admire more— the incredible track or the magnificently capable men who ran it.

10

SUPERSONIC BASEBALL

But Not Like the World Series

THE EUROPEAN YEARS of missile obscurity had been drifting farther and farther behind—while the blazing white clarity of the American Desert sprang up on every side. Nothing could have been more different. Nowhere in the world could there have been more contradictions. In fact like the missiles and everything else of man's creating as he reached for the stars and at least fingered the star dust, life in the dusty Southwest had its corresponding ups and downs.

Some of it seemed as stark and terrifying as the wild missile blasts themselves. Wind storms like a thousand banshees howling down the desolate canyons. Dust storms as dense as fog and as abrasive as grinding tools. The thorny flora—ocotillo, staghorn, prickly pear, hedgehog, devil's finger, yucca, cholla, ironwood; the restless tumbleweed rolling endlessly across the landscape until caught and impaled by barbed wire; the giant saguaros like inarticulate plant monsters marching with ungainly arms waving vainly to the skies; a thousand Joshua trees in stunted neurotic shapes twisted by the wind and gnarled by the sun. Also the thorny or hissing or slithering *fauna*—horned toads, Gila monsters, the angry scorpion, the hairy spider, the reptilian coil and rattle under the neighboring mesquite bush. A grotesque land, a land for trolls and misfits, more awesome than the Nibelungen land. Where Alberich would have done well, and the gnomes under the Rhein. (Yet would the dry river beds have taken the place of their *Rheinflüss?*)

And then the exquisite, feathery, sometime flowering of the desert. With countless hues and varieties—cactus blooms, like beauty out of ancient beginnings, flowering yucca and barrel cacti, skeleton-weed, Indian paintbrush, carpets of yellow poppy, splashes of purple sand verbena, splotches of blue lupine, the golds and pinks and clarets of rattleweed and pincushion and brittlebush, the miles upon miles of tall road-bordering sunflowers. A riot of colors—and above it another riot, the sunsets. Of orange and purple and lavender, saffron and chartreuse and mottle-green, unbelievable mixtures painted above the jagged hills, or flying their pastel banners across the enchanted heavens. The Land of Enchantment the natives called it—and some of the missileers who came also liked what they saw and were likewise enchanted and captivated.

There were other attractions—and contrasts. For instance in a Chamber of Commerce folder one could read: "Here you may lunch on the side of a mountain or in caverns far below the earth's surface, angle for your own trout meal or dine in the most modern restaurant, ski on powdery snow or romp in clean warm sands, relax at a desert guest ranch or explore a historic river valley—all in this land of vividly contrasting cultures, Indian, Spanish, Anglo-Saxon, now blended together in the ultra-modern Space Age. Here in the Southwest you can listen to the beat of a tom-tom, a gay folk song brought centuries ago from old Spain, a lonesome cowboy ballad—and sense yourself in the world of tomorrow by the nearness of America's most advanced scientific and research sites."

Words as flowery as the desert itself—and yet basically quite true!

For instance twenty miles from Alamogordo were the lofty pines and hills of the Sacramentos, four hours drive over those hills the world-famous caverns of Carlsbad, a few miles beyond Holloman the snowy dunes of White Sands, an hour's drive northward the winter resort of Ruidoso with real snow and the ski runs of 12,000-foot Sierra Blanca. There were trout streams all through the hills, old ranches and ghost towns along the flatlands, historic battlegrounds where Geronimo's Apaches had fought it out with the U.S. Cavalry and lost, Wild West festivals in Tularosa where Billy the Kid had outlawed himself and paid the price. There was Old Mexico less than a hundred miles to the south, Taos with its ancient Pueblos to the north, El Paso del Norte or the "pass to the north" of the Conquistadors who settled "La Villa Real de la Santa Fé de San Francisco" (the Royal City of the Holy Faith of Saint Francis) before the English landed at Plymouth Rock. And now there were the bustling modern cities of several hundred thousand inhabitants, El Paso, Albuquerque along the same ancient trail, Santa Fe a bit farther on with less people but more of the old flavor of its origins; there were Hilton Hotels and plush motels, bars and diners, churches and schools, drive-in theatres and opera houses, symphony orchestras and civic bodies—and the great cattle ranges replaced by the great missile range, with its leaping and thundering rockets.

Where the faithful horse and its rider of the old West had once pushed themselves to the limit for a hundred miles a day there were now sleek metal vehicles covering the same distance in moments.

Locally also the charming travel folders could play up this contrast. For instance in an Alamogordo version one could read: "We now have a cosmopolitan city of more than 25,000 people, in which the newer inhabitants have come from all over the world to work at Holloman Air Force Base. And one thing they're delighted with is our climate."

And again this was true. There were also the cool and refreshing mornings. The city itself nestled so closely against the Sacramento foothills towering some few thousand feet higher that it was almost reminiscent of Bavarian cities, Bad Reichenhall, Ettal, Oberammergau, except that every street was excellently flat for bicycling and the many snowy peaks were regrettably absent.

Before such things as bombing ranges and missiles Alamogordo had been a lumber town—a small railroad had ambled back into the hills and sawmills had been operating as early as the turn of the century. Yet as late as 1945 its population still numbered only a few thousands. Then had come Holloman—named like so many other bases in honor of one of its distinguished airmen. (A fine practice of the Air Force.) In this instance for Colonel George V. Holloman, who had died in a B-17 crash in the Far East, on Formosa. The Holloman name had been conferred in 1948. And as the missiles had changed the old bombing range, so Holloman had changed Alamogordo.

It had also changed the place known as Cloudcroft, in the hills above Alamogordo—the one spot above all that Holloman came to for its off-days and weekends, the most accessible, the nearest mountain resort area where could be had relief even from the blazing desert. Once it too had been a lumber station, but now it served as the hub of a great national park area, the Lincoln National Forest, a magnificent region of immense old pines, aspens like showers of gold in the autumn, wooded hills and valleys full of summer horseback trails and winter ski runs, picnic grounds so popular that half the car license plates showed a Texas origin.

At the Cloudcroft apex stood a fine first-class hotel called The Lodge, which had proved ideal for Holloman's visiting firemen and their scientific symposiums. It also boasted of having the highest golf course in the United States—9,000 feet above sea level, a truly majestic sweep of greens and fairways rimmed by the immense pines through a natural upland valley—where every Hollomanite with a set of irons itched mightily to play and undoubtedly did.

Nevertheless to get back to Holloman itself, the fact was that even its excursions were only the briefest interludes to its real life, the part that was its Space Age life. So that even the excitement of playing a high-altitude golf game at Cloudcroft could hardly match (for one example) the excitement other people had been having with a "supersonic ball game" at Holloman.

Or at least not when one knew what the ball game was all about.

The project engineers had dubbed it "Catcher's Mitt." But ball fans or not, they certainly had never seen its like either on a sandlot or in a World Series park. For the ball was a live artillery shell. The bat a 155-millimeter howitzer cannon. As for the pitcher, that happened to be a millisecond-timed trigger system. And the catcher? Only a rocket sled—moving at supersonic speeds just like the ball.

Among all the activities cramming the Holloman scene with rocket blasts, drone tests, sonic booms, stratosphere balloon launches, missile flights, and other such events—probably none had ever rivaled for sheer novelty and ingenuity the project known as Catcher's Mitt. From the beginning it had been completely unique. There were no records of its ever having been tried before. And Holloman had been selected by the project's sponsors for one reason—the 35,000-foot captive-missile test track.

On morning after morning as the sun gleamed along the track's polished rails and lit up the north-end safety blockhouse (Blockhouse Coco), the small group of project experts could be seen with the bizarre accoutrements for their game—the sled, the howitzer, the cannon shells—working out the incredible time-and-placement operations that were to accomplish such an unheard of feat.

The experts had gathered from several places. The project coordinator Bill Guillorn was from Picatinny Arsenal in New Jersey. Project engineer Ralph Vecchio was from the same outfit. Ordnance engineer Jake Sine came from the Aberdeen Proving Grounds. Also instrumentation specialist Stan Keen. A crack howitzer team was also there from Aberdeen. A hot rocket crew headed by Technical Sergeant Marion Miller was Holloman's own, as was the over-all supervising engineer, Captain Morris Haven—who was fond of saying, more in wry fun than strict truth: "I'm only living and sleeping and breathing this project, that's all."

"Moe" Haven along with his track boss Colonel Don Vlcek had, in addition to the project's other problems, not a small one of their own: the responsibility of keeping a $12 million test track from damage caused by howitzer shells or otherwise.

The whole thing had begun with the need of finding some way to recover artillery shells intact and undamaged. Ordnance experts had long been trying to determine firing effects entirely separate from impact effects, especially with ultra-high-powered modern ammunition. Various schemes had already been tried. For example using a landing bed of water. For another, straight-up firing and parachute recovery without the shell landing anywhere. For another, shell-and-parachute catch by a probe device on a flying aircraft. None had worked.

Whoever hit first on the supersonic sled idea for a soft-cushion artillery catch was not exactly known, at any rate to the people engaged in the Holloman experiment. But most of them admitted having had a hand (or thought) in it. From there the idea, like Topsy, had just growed. News of the Holloman track and its supersonic abilities (like those of bullets and high-powered shells) had completed the imaginative picture, launching the ordnance-inspired dreams like rockets probing for unknown frontiers.

So the game—or the work—had begun. So, too, the project had become a joint Army-Air Force operation from the word go. The 155 mm howitzer had been freighted in to Holloman from Aberdeen. The specially designed sled, built to rush specifications in six weeks by Aircraft Armament Incorporated, was trucked from Cockyville, Maryland. Meanwhile the sled's rocket boosters, four for each firing, 50,000-pound-thrust giants intended for a total of 200,000 pounds for each run (more by a quarter than the IRBM Thor had needed for its thrust into space) had been shipped in from Picatinny.

One look at the sled when it arrived had been enough to explain the need for the herculean thrust. It was 19 feet long. Six feet high. Almost as wide. Its weight over 10,000 pounds. Built like a box car, tapered only at the front, it was the largest contraption ever scheduled up to that time for a run on the Holloman track. After that one look everyone had the same comment: "It'll never get off the ground!" In fact even before its first test run it was dubbed—and remained—"The Monster."

But that first run did not come off so quickly. There were still all kinds of problems.

For instance the "catcher's mitt" idea had to be worked out. The catching compartment was almost as wide and high and long as The Monster itself. What was to be used inside to cushion it? The answer at last was solidly packed foam rubber, celotex, and polyurethane plastic. A man would have bounced into that gently enough from a three-story building. (No man tried it!) But would a faster-than-sound moving cannon shell?

There was also the problem of gun emplacement. A high-powered explosive shell flies high. There's a curved trajectory. The plan and trajectory both had to be straightened out for a long flat skimming flight parallel to the earth. So the gun mount was sunk 39 inches into a hole dug through the track's concrete apron itself, then bulwarked at sides and back with heavy sandbags. The flatness would keep the peak trajectory within the limits of the moving sled structure, the sandbags (hopefully) would minimize blast against the track.

Since the track also dropped one foot in every thousand going in a southerly direction—and the runs had to be south to keep stray artillery shells from landing in other directions—this too had to be compensated for.

The Aberdeen experts had the answer to this one. Using their ordnance lore they calculated the total gun elevation at 10.6 mils. (A mil being that unit of angular measurement which is equal to $1/6400$ of a 360-degree circle—as at least ordnance experts knew.)

But the problem of emplacement also had to avoid artillery damage to the track. Meaning, if the catcher muffed the ball—if the sled failed to catch the shell—what then of the precision-built infinitely precious test track?

This only added to further complications. The sandbags might help against direct shell blast, but there was also the shell's impact to be considered.

Presently it was decided that in digging the gun in alongside the track it would also be aimed on a slight diagonal that would come within the track configuration only during a fraction of the sled run. Which of course meant that shell and sled could come together only within that same space and time—moving a bit crosswise and at supersonic speeds!

So the original difficulties had become child's play compared with what yet had to be calculated. The really basic problem was one of relativity—relative velocities. The shell traveled 1,650 feet per second. (Or better than 1,100 miles an hour.) It was found that The Monster, even with its giant booster, dawdled along at a mere 1,450 to 1,550 feet per second. (In other words a mere 1,000 miles an hour.)

With only this much to go on, the real calculations began.

It was already evident that if the sled was fired first (somewhere near the gun of course) the higher velocity of the shell would enable it to catch up with the sled at some given point ahead. Also that if the gun could be triggered by the sled, then relative velocities and distances could be equated against a given place and time. Then if at that given place and time the two velocities were almost equal, the soft catch with no impact effects could be made.

How Einstein might have loved working out that one!

In his absence the project Einsteins worked it out their own way. The firing point for the sled was fixed 1,936 feet to the rear of the gun. In approaching the gun the sled was equipped to actuate a trigger-timing mechanism and then a second mechanism precisely 86 feet beyond the first. The firing of the gun would occur only by reaching a pre-determined velocity with the sled. The sled's velocity would have to move it between the two switch points in 59 milliseconds. A tolerance of one millisecond (1/1000 of a second) either way, but no more, would still allow the firing of the gun. When the gun was fired, all the further calculations would bring the shell up to the sled 900 feet ahead, at relative velocities of about 125 feet per second, for a catch along the next 361 feet of track before the shell diagonaled over the track and beyond. After a catch the sled would coast to a stop about 20,000 feet from its starting point.

To reduce this to the miraculous: what such calculations really meant was that the "catcher" could get the "ball" only within 17/1000 of a second—while both traveled at speeds better than 17 miles a minute!

The odd thing about it was that the miracle worked. Not only once, but every time.

It was really unique. In the superbly clear southwest sunshine the Picatinny-Aberdeen-Holloman team worked day after day at the track, calculating and recalculating. Guillorn and Vecchio, Sine and Keen, Miller and Haven, and others. Frequently the colonel himself was there. (Sometimes the curious writer.) Everyone in the Track Test Division had remained curious—the quiet bets and good-natured comments had never let up.

Nine times they fired The Monster. Six times the howitzer. And on all six synchro-firings the catch was made.

The catches could have been made more frequently. Except for what happens even to the best-laid plans of mice and men. For the problems had still piled up, even from firing to firing. The ungainly width of The Monster posed one such teaser. On its very first run (with many eyes besides the project crew's peering from the long narrow Blockhouse Coco slit as its squat bulk and long flame tail disappeared down the track) it was found that in streaking past the sandbags it had popped its rivets like Frankenstein coming loose at the seams. Reflected shock wave had caused the damage. But heavier rivets solved this problem—probably the easiest one in the entire project.

But still other problems kept materializing. On the fourth run (the first synchro-run) the 120-pound "ball" went clean through the "mitt" and landed somewhere in the desert.

"Among the boondocks," said Moe Haven wryly. "Rolling around in the sand. Good thing it wasn't a live shell—that's why we have to try dummies first. Not much damage to the shell though—the Aberdeen analysts said they're glad to get it."

For this sticker a steel plate and two-inch plywood were used to back up the padding in The Monster's "mitt." But on the next run the "ball" smacked into the steel. The answer was padding that would stop the 10,000-rpm spin of the shell from acting like an angry electric drill—the only problem that never became perfectly solved.

Trouble was also caused by the variable rocket boosters, or rather by the shell contacting before the elimination of the afterburner blast. On the sixth of the nine runs it knocked a piece of hot booster nozzle into the sled causing the padding to ignite; on the seventh run, booster blast did the same. The only answer to this would have been a catch after full burn-out; in other words higher sled velocity to lengthen the critical part of the curve where "ball" and "mitt" should meet.

Nevertheless in spite of all such minor obstacles the catches were made. Every time. On the ninth run, for the first time, a live shell was used. Again it was a bull's-eye. Every calculation had been taken care of, all further corrections effected, the miracle itself accomplished. In short, ballistics and rockets, artillery and aeronautics, the Army and the Air Force had teamed up to play a supersonic ball game—and had won.

Now what golf game at Cloudcroft could have been more exciting than that?

11

ROCKET SLEDS

The Fastest Thing on Earth

"You once asked me if the Russians had a track like ours and I said if so they'd kept it a better secret than Sputnik," the colonel remarked. "But as a matter of fact they do have one."

I had to remember a long way back, and marvel at his own unusual memory.

"The news came out lately when a U.S. aeromedical group visited Russia. The Soviet scientists told the story—it's a three-railed track, with a water-braking system and at least a Mach two sled. The three-railed technique is supposed to give a more stable ride."

The round good-natured Vlcek face behind its inevitable short pipe was the face of a friend by this time. Admittedly an appreciative one since supersonic ball games and other track wonders had been a bit more in the public news.

"Is it in fact a more stable ride?" I asked.

"At least it sounds reasonable. The U.S. Navy was going to build one as its SNORT track but never did. A long time back Italy was going to build a test track. We sent over Warren Sanders and Dick Chandler—Chandler was a lieutenant at the time and is now one of our best engineers who just helped design our latest and biggest sled, the liquid-oxygen Rocketdyne. After their advisory trip the Italian scheme fell through—probably because of the same sort of costs we have to justify."

We were standing on the roof of the Midway building on a day long past our first meetings and it was the RS-2 Rocketdyne sled we had just watched as it made one of its early checkout runs. On the Midway roof, two stories high, which was often a spectator area for visitors, one saw more of the track's intricate communication network. Two 30-foot steel masts stood at opposite corners for line-of-sight transmission from any point along the track. The meshed ladder and double saucers of an 800-megacycle directional-type antenna were there for the same purpose. Before climbing to the roof I had also glimpsed the latest developments in the Midway interior and heard more about its architectural wonders. Built over a wire mesh foundation that formed a part of its radio shield, it was a completely windowless building. From the inside, air pressure half a pound higher than the ambient atmosphere forced air outward to prevent dust intake—in fact dust, temperature, and humidity were under permanent control to protect the hundreds of Midway instruments.

But it was the supersensitive instruments that were the real marvel. Long banks of them stood in every room and as we walked about, accompanied by the lean-jawed, unruly-haired instrumentation chief, Major Ursel Nolte, the only way they could be described seemed to be in terms including all the mysteries of electronics per se.

I knew the instrumentation consisted mainly of three telemetry systems, a pulse duration modulation system known as the PDM, a frequency modulation system known as FM/FM, and a pulse code modulation system, the PCM, all working in the 800-828 megacycle range to lessen frequency interference with other activities in the Holloman area.

("Telemetry," the major patiently explained, "is simply the technique of recording or viewing distant events by such things as meter readings and transmitting the data from a distance by electromagnetic means. Typically the system contains pickups which convert the instrument readings or mechanical actions into electrical pulses and feed them into the radio transmitter or another kind of telemetering link. The link may be common wire, special cable, a light beam, an ultra-violet beam—but usually it's a radio transmitter and receiver. The telemeter recorder can be a simple oscilloscope, a revolving drum with a recording stylus, or just an automatic tape recorder. The results are fed into IBM machines or punched on cards or stored in tubes or put on magnetic tape."

"Which makes telemetry one of the most useful tools of modern science," the colonel gently added. "In fact without telemetry and the computer output we get from Holloman's data reduction center all our work would be completely wasted.")

There was much more to be learned about the three telemetry systems, or ground stations. All three received their track data by means of sled-borne telemetry packages equipped with transmitters and various sensors (such as voltage meters and strain gauges) to carry separate channels of information from the sled to the Midway recording instruments. The PDM system with ten channels for real-time display and 88 available for automatic separation was used when many points of static information were needed. The FM/FM system with its seven-track tape units and 48 separate channels for data transmission was called the work-horse of the track.

The PCM system came in for special comment. One of the most advanced digital telemetering systems in existence, with data-gathering accuracies up to 99.8 percent, it had been designed expressly for the Holloman track. Built largely of transistors and other solid-state devices for reliability and small-package requirements, its 32 channels could gather as many as 264,000 bits of information during each second of a sled run. This was accomplished by means of an analog transducer or power-crossing output received by the sled-borne equipment, coded into digital form for transmission through the PCM channels, and received at the ground station for quick-look results and selection of parts of each tape for fuller analysis. The tapes were then carried, still in their raw form, to the data reduction center, translated for entry into one of the computers, and reduced to tabular, plotted, or punchcard form for final analysis.

"Which can be clarified in another way by saying"—the Vlcek words issued like light cast into dark corners—"the validity of all our track test data depends on the data's ability to determine and define the time relationship of given events—and that's where the final work of the computers comes in. Our timing-and-programming system is another part of the same operation—it has to provide what we call timing reference signals, in other words the programming of on-off operations for cameras, instrumentation, countdowns, the actual firing—making sure that each event takes place in its proper time sequence so that it can be accurately defined for later analysis of the test data. For our track events the system provides time pulses ranging all the way from one pulse per thousand seconds up to five millions pulses for a single second. And if you think that's unbelievable—some day go over and see what the Holloman computers and the data reduction center are doing!"

I had already been there on cursory visits. But, as in the Midway building, I had become as lost as a single pulse seeking its way through the five million.

There were other matters to be learned about the track. In fact the story of the track itself, from its first modest use of a truss-frame rocket sled with a single low-thrust, solid-fuel booster for propulsion, to its later giant-size, liquid-fuel, sled-and-engine vehicles some of which could deliver nearly a third of a million pounds of variable and controllable thrust, was the story of a space age tool forged in the heat of countless trials, experiments, design and engineering problems, exotic fuel hazards, and always expanding projects crowding in every kind of track test from the catching of a flying artillery shell to the simulated flight of an entire missile guidance system.

Perhaps its origins, like its growth, were just as inevitable as the Space Age. A mild climate, daily sunshine, a dry hard lake bed as old as the geology of the Pleistocene, parallel rows of mountain ranges some 50 miles apart enclosing a natural earthquake-free basin of flatland almost a mile above sea level; these were the built-in features. In turn they had led to the selecting of Holloman as one of the Air Research and Development Command's (later the Air Force Systems Command's) outstanding research sites, home of the Air Force Missile Development Center. And as surely as missiles had to be taught to fly, and tested in any number of ways to make sure of that flight effectiveness, the idea of Holloman's captive-missile test track had been born.

In 1950 its length had been only 3,550 feet. But missiles then were also in their diaper days. During that year several prototype Snark missiles were bolted to rocket sleds and blasted along the track in the first great demonstration of what its engineers began to call "pre-flight testing and recovery of the test item"—a new era in missile research, saving countless tax dollars through wringing out design and performance faults in missiles, guidance systems, component parts, instrumentation, in short all the hardware of a vehicle ultimately intended for either aerodynamic or space flight.

That this electronic freight was not the only cargo the new "railroad" could carry was also soon demonstrated, for by 1954 it was carrying passengers—first chimpanzees, then Colonel John Paul Stapp in his famous windblast and deceleration rides which not only added to his own stature as a scientist but opened up more far-reaching uses for the track itself.

From then on the impetus gathered. By 1957 the track had reached its planned length of 35,000 feet, and by 1959, when it was officially opened by the man who perhaps had done more than any other to support it, Holloman's one-time commander, Major General Leighton I. Davis (later in command of the National Range Division of which Cape Kennedy is a part), more than 250 people made up its working staff of electronic, mechanical, aeronautical, metallurgical, and chemical engineers, skilled mechanics, technicians, draftsmen, and other assistants.

There were noteworthy facts also about its many types of sleds and sled runs—and as time went on the facts accumulated.

During that same year of 1959 one of its slim monorail sleds fired in two stages by a Cajun and four Loki rockets during slipper-wear tests reached a top speed of 3,090 miles an hour—better than four times the speed of sound.

A bullet-shaped single-stage Pershing sled weighing 7,500 pounds and carrying a 1,400-pound payload to test missile warhead fusing systems made another speed record for sleds of its type and size by moving 1,926 miles an hour—nearly three times the speed of a .45 calibre bullet.

A 21-inch-high wedge-pointed monorail model was fitted with a pair of 23-inch inertially activated brake fins designed to fan out automatically under windblast; with a powerful 73,000-pound thrust from a cluster of solid-propellant Javelin rockets, it sped 2,650 miles an hour and built up a force of 50 G's during acceleration, 63 G's during the time its airbrakes operated at full deceleration, to demonstrate a new system of braking monorail sleds.

One of the largest and heaviest monorail sleds ever built, a 2½-ton three-stage vehicle 48 feet long—looking like a giant string of sausages before its Nike boosters ignited one stage after the other to create a mile-long flame tail—again broke all velocity records for its kind as it traveled 3½ times the speed of sound before hurtling off the end of the track into a prepared block of concrete: an impact test to prove out Army ordnance warheads.

By 1960 the track was able to celebrate its thousandth successful sled run.

By 1962 it reached what was undoubtedly one of its proudest moments when the Air Force Systems Command made it the directing agency for all Air Force track activities.

In October 1963 it celebrated its two thousandth sled run—and at almost the same time chalked up another memorable milepost when specially designed spike-monorail sleds began speeding along the track at hypersonic velocities, in other words more than five times the speed of sound.

Moreover it had not only become busier; a still wider variety of experiments proved its growing versatility as a research tool, as well as the increased sophistication with which its "gang of railroaders" were finding and developing its uses.

For example a series of runs to evaluate rain erosion effects on space vehicles during reentry conditions was accomplished with a gooseneck-fronted monorail sled that resembled some strange new space bird itself as it carried various types of nose cones at Mach three velocities through

6,000 feet of trackside "rain" simulated by a double row of 1,500 nozzles spraying a total of 5,000 gallons per minute—the most unusual such test area ever constructed.

A 3,000-pound dual-rail sled built in the Holloman maintenance shops to test a spacecraft's landing gear carried its ungainly pyramid-like framework and hydraulically suspended test item (the landing gear) through another long series of track runs with landings simulated on three types of runway surfaces, dry lake bed, asphalt, and concrete—temporarily different surfaces moulded into the track bed itself.

An Army project to guide an anti-tank missile to its target by electrical signals communicated through trailing wires was tested with a 370-pound monorail sled fashioned with an outrigger to carry non-rotating drums off which the test wire unwound as a fishing rod spins line off a reel.

An elaborately designed sled vehicle built like an aircraft cockpit, with fore-and-aft ejection seats, was used in any number of projects by seating well-instrumented anthropomorphic dummies inside, blasting the sled down the track, and allowing the dummies to hurtle skyward (building up vertical and longitudinal high-G accelerations as well as other stresses) to prove the effectiveness of various aircraft escape systems.

To study spacecraft takeoff and reentry conditions, more sophisticated acceleration-deceleration-vibration sled runs used passengers again in the form of chimpanzees—an ancient project that had started with Stapp and had even put chimps Ham and Enos through such paces before they were blasted from Cape Canaveral in Project Mercury space capsules to become the most famous animals of their kind. Later versions of such tests gathered a wealth of data that contributed richly to the Gemini and Apollo moon-landing space programs.

Another ingenious idea involved the question of what would happen to a space vehicle reentering the earth's atmosphere if it encountered a nuclear blast. This was really a knotty one for the engineers. To create and measure such effects a narrow four-sided plywood shock tube 150 feet long was built off the end of the track. The tube was pumped full of Freon gas and tightly sealed, thus creating a dense gas environment. A supersonic monorail sled carrying a nose cone was blasted along the track and into the tube; at the same instant a high-explosive charge was set off at the other end of the tube. By the time the tube was splintering into pure debris the sled met the TNT blast, interior instruments measured the effects—and a little more was known about what might happen to a spacecraft.

But in fact all the ideas were ingenious and unique—and the more one talked with the "gang of railroaders," listened to their problems, watched the kaleidoscope of track runs, dug out the tortuous details, the more one marveled. Though another marvel entirely had to do with sheer brute power, and the liquid-engine sleds. The real giants. Capable of pushing entire missile guidance systems, and built specially for that purpose.

No solid-propellant rocket propulsion, as the track people had found, could give the smooth or prolonged burning characteristics needed in wringing out the secrets of an inertial guidance system's gyros and accelerometers and other delicate instruments devised to make a missile go accurately from here to there. On the other hand the powerful liquid-engines with their variable thrust and great payload-carrying forebody-sleds could do just this. Thus there had been the RS-1, then the RS-2, then the AJ-10, the CEC-2200, all veritable Gargantuas among sled vehicles, roaring along the track with thrust chambers wide open spitting out smoke and flame like boilers created for more hellish regions.

Some, like the Rocketdynes, used liquid oxygen as an oxidizer with 75% alcohol and 25% water as fuel, a pressurizing medium of helium, and a single uncooled thrust chamber.

Others like the Aerojet and Coleman engines were triple-chambered behemoths weighing as much as seven to eight tons. Consisting mainly of a fuel tank, an oxidizing tank, immense vertically lined thrust chambers and a complicated system of electrical, hydraulic, and propulsion units all built upon a powerful steel framework, these 24-foot monsters used a propellant of inhibited red fuming nitric acid (the oxidizer) combined with UDMH (unsymmetrical dimethylhydrazine) and JP-4 (jet fuel) to push a 4,000-pound sled forebody with enormous acceleration up to 1,200 miles an hour while sled-borne and trackside instruments collected as high as 90 channels of guidance system data such as vibration and strain gauge information, accelerometer output, inertial platform attitude, system-measured velocity and other precious facts needed to improve a missile's steering.

So mighty indeed were these monsters among engines (and looking not too unlike the railroad article itself!) that in terms of G forces or gravity pull they could start accelerating at eight times their own weight. They could also be stopped at fifteen times their weight as they ploughed through the track's water dams, with an underslung scoop transferring momentum away from the sled.

Moreover as the track's propulsion chief Marvin Weber said, with his own brand of whimsy: "They did more than Casey's Cannonball Express even in railroad terms, for they carried the most expensive part of a missile—its guidance system—through every one of these runs without a single freight damage bill."

And so the Holloman track had grown—in fame and significance as well as linear dimensions. With its liquid-fuel engines it had first tested the ICBM Minuteman's guidance systems and uncovered defects that could have lost a missile; a test result that caused rejoicing when the first Minuteman ever fired at Cape Canaveral was a complete success, and brought even more pride when General Bernard Schriever, the boss of all Air Force Systems Command research and development, publicly acknowledged the Holloman track's part in that success.

Likewise there had been all the later-phase Minuteman tests, for advanced guidance systems. Also for the Atlas, Titan, Skybolt, Centaur. Also the Saturn, NASA's multimillion-pound-thrust booster for its lunar expeditions. Famous missiles and their warhead fuzing systems like those of the Pershing, Bullpup, Littlejohn had been impact-tested off the end of the track time and again. Tests for aerodynamic stress, acceleration, deceleration, vibration, instrument performance, biophysical hazards and many other space flight problems had by now become the track's bread-and-butter work. Its talented technicians had devised innumerable methods for accomplishing test objectives. The tests simulated as closely as possible the conditions under which each test package was expected to perform; except for impact tests the test item was almost invariably recovered for the most detailed physical scrutiny; complete photo coverage as well as electronic data were also gathered to provide the nation's missile and spacecraft makers with what they needed to know.

Thus it was not too surprising that by the end of 1965 even the linear-dimension thought had expanded; negotiations were already under way by then, even a design completed, for adding another 500 feet to the pair of shining steel rails extending far out to the north of Holloman with scrubby brown desert on one side and miles of glistening white sand on the other.

No, the Space Age limits were nowhere!

Or as it was stated by Colonel Lawrence H. Ballweg, the track chief at that time, in one of our many talks while his face lit up with the same serious intensity I had found in other dedicated people at Holloman: "We really have to look ahead all the time—and we have to keep ahead. I don't think it's too far-fetched to say we're really in business here for the nation, at least that part of it occupied with space research. Fifteen years is a long time as track testing goes, and we've emerged as the chief agency in the free world for that. For instance who would have

thought a few years ago"—his smile broadened, became almost a grin—
"that in 1965, with an orbiting Gemini capsule overhead, the Holloman
track would be selected to perform an experiment with a smoking
belching sled run so nicely tied in with NASA's world global system that
the astronauts could not only spot and recognize the track, but tell the
whole world about it? That's a little of what I mean."

12

THE BIRDCATCHER

What a Pound of Feathers Can Do

NEVERTHELESS, in the midst of even this spectacular progress,
there was at least one fly in the ointment. Or to be more exact, not a
fly but birds. The ointment being the Holloman test track itself—where
the birds came to roost.

Of all the minor problems that had come to beset the track's astute
engineers, problems like slipper wear, broken plugs, faulty circuits,
snapping wires—and of all the absurd problems that could plague a
mighty super-science operation right up to its proudest moments and
most dignified achievements—the bird problem at the track had always
been the plaguiest.

The birds liked the track. Its high rails and full splashy braking troughs
were their only watering place—their Riviera, Bar Harbor, resort spa all
in one. The troughs might have been built for nothing but parched and
thirsty bird throats. Even the filtering desert sands could have been intended as the most deluxe of bird baths.

And the result? Both bird casualties and sled casualties.

Ever since the days of supersonic sled speeds it had been happening.
At such velocities the birds never even heard the sleds coming. Which
not only ruined their resort plans; the other sad and fantastic outcome
was dented and twisted sled shapes or even gaping holes in the solid
steel itself.

For such was the phenomenon of high-velocity impact. Just as the force of a hurricane could drive a splinter through a solid tree trunk, or a grain-sized meteorite could blast its way through a traveling space-craft, so a rocket sled moving several times the speed of sound had its own collision hazards to deal with. And while collision with a pound of feathers was not as serious as the crash of a jet aircraft invaded by a flock of starlings, the damage to a costly sled or its precious payload was serious enough in terms of scientific research, in fact even in terms of lost taxpayer money.

As an example of such damage, a 212-pound sled going 3,000 miles an hour had ended its run with a jagged ten-inch hole torn right through its quarter inch armor-plate steel. A 4,700-pound sled finished its 850-mph run with its half-inch sheathing torn loose along the bolted seams. A 160-pound sled streaking along at 2,850 miles an hour reached a stop with its wedgelike steel prow dented in at least four inches. A 375-pound sled clocked at 1,500 miles an hour was almost derailed when one of its inch-thick steel slippers was forced almost entirely open.

All this was caused by sudden impact with small feathered creatures—doves, pigeons, quail, weighing perhaps a pound apiece. Not that it happened with every sled run. But when even one bird alighted to preen, or fluttered up from a trough, something was bound to happen.

And it still seemed absurd.

From time to time the problem had been discussed.

"It's the zaniest one we've ever faced," was the comment of a super-visor, Bob Rethmel. "Sometimes the impact pre-triggers instruments or knocks out a telemetry recorder. And with our liquid engines it could really be serious—fuel lines maybe struck, engine malfunction, velocity offsets—and at least the cost of the entire run over again."

From time to time the problem had been tackled.

"For a little while we thought of poison," remarked Major Dave Kahne, "but that would have been both messy and inhumane."

"Something we did come up with was the idea of animal or bird cries or loud sharp noises—anything to scare 'em," said Major Don Jones.

"All we've needed of course is to get them off the track those few seconds in which the sled goes by," said Major Don Cole.

The ideas had been tried.

"We've wired our loudspeaker system which has amplifiers at every thousand feet along the track," said instrumentation chief Warren Sanders. "Just before a sled run we crank in our sound effects."

"Two special effects we've bought are a machine gun record and a thunder record," said photographer Hugh Ferguson.

"And Indian war cries," added his assistant, Mrs. Frankie Wilson.

Apparently the birds weren't too impressed.

"There's an ornithologist at Cornell University we've heard about," said Captain Walter Hoy. "He's been recording bird cries for years."

"We understand he has one record that actually caught a hawk coming in for the kill—wild screech, victim's squawks, everything," said Lieutenant Bernard Jackson.

"We think if we amplify that along the track it might scare every little bird for miles," said design engineer Jim Tubb.

"Except another hawk," morosely added track scheduler Pat Brown.

"Anyway we've written the professor," said engineer chief Joe Mapes.

But the hawk cries didn't work too well either.

"We've got it!" cried engineer Bill Chambers one day. "There's a bird-chasing outfit up north, the Roost-Not-Here Company. One thing they do is spread goo all over the perching places—too sticky even for birds. "We've sent for them."

The Roost-Not-Here experts came, saw—and failed to conquer. Besides messing up the track rails just as stickily.

"The carbide cannons we've procured should do the trick," said project officer Harry Best as he busied himself with placement calculations. "By a gas and water intake and flash triggering we'll simulate so many shotgun blasts they'll think it's the end of the Bird Kingdom."

But the bird kingdom still survived.

"We're going to try everything at once," grimly said Lieutenant Colonel Larry Bogard (who at this time in the long Bird War—before the time of Ballweg—was also presiding over the track). "Machine gun fire, battle sounds, hawk cries, cannons—everything!"

"And we do mean everything," added track project engineer Berle Engle.

But the campaign continued.

The birds simply weren't disturbed enough.

Such was the state of affairs, long after the preliminary skirmishes, long after the dignity of having become the Air Force's track directing agency, when the best brains in the track division finally had to go into a huddle to outwit the bird brains.

All the king's men if not all the king's horses were busy at it—Rethmel, Kahne, Jones, Cole, Sanders, Ferguson, Hoy, Chandler, Tubb, Brown, Mapes, Chambers, Best, Bogard, Engle, Wayne Roemersberger, Hans Rasmussen, Sam Fletcher, Marvin Weber, Lieutenant Lou Kingsland, Lieutenant John Friel, Lieutenant Warren Fitzgerald, Captain

George Watts, Captain Ernie Miller—in truth almost as many thinkers as birds.

And the solution was found.

Since nothing had cleared the birds entirely away, it was reasoned that a non-payload sled could be fired a few seconds before the payload-bearing sled to shoo the birds off the track just long enough for the real test run to be made before they fluttered back to their rails and roosting places.

In the end it seemed as simple as the trick of Columbus balancing the egg.

Though after the slim six-foot monorail sled—inevitably called the Bird Catcher—had been designed and built, the almost simultaneous firing just prior to the firing of a second sled presented other problems, principally in braking and timing.

A timing device was originated that would fire two sleds just five seconds apart, at almost the same starting point on the track. This was done by means of the track's timing-and-programming system, briefly as follows: firing the first sled, controlling the time clock in an automatic hold, tripping a breakwire with the first sled 1,970 feet farther (a 1.25-second time interval) to restart the clock, thereby causing a completed countdown and the firing of the second sled. Distance and sled velocities were meticulously calculated to make the timing accurate.

The next problem was that of stopping the first sled, the Bird Catcher. With high velocities needed to keep it from loitering in the way of the second sled, some braking device had to be created to stop it from running off the end of the track altogether. The design of the bird-shooing sled included this consideration. Just behind and above its duckbill-shaped nose (the duckbill was non-revengeful, sheer coincidence, just plain good sled design) a steel T had been built that would catch and hold the sled against straps. The straps were made of web-nylon in long enough lengths to stretch above and across the track rails like a Navy flattop's elastic plane barriers. Suspended a few inches in the air by poles on either side of the rails, the straps slid along the sloping front end of the sled, bounced against the steel T—and the Bird Catcher in turn was caught.

To guarantee that it would stop, three long strap barriers were placed one after the other at 30-foot distances along the end of the track, on the theory that if one broke, three would not. The theory proved correct.

The theories behind the Bird Catcher also proved correct. Without instrumentation but with velocity profiles checked by Berkeley counters and fast-working ribbon-frame cameras the sled was fired in combination enough times to indicate that very few birds would get in the way of future sled runs.

And so there was great rejoicing in the land—the people were no longer downcast and honor had been restored unto them.

Verily the ways of the Lord—and the Holloman track testers—had been proved great.

13

THE BOPPER

John Paul Stapp and His Giant Slingshot

ALTHOUGH FOR A CURIOUS REPORTER (and, as it turned out, for other news gatherers coming in from time to time after clearing the Washington channels) the chimpanzees were easily the most colorful part of aeromedical activities, they were by no means the only part, nor was the Holloman zoo the only answer to the many problems.

Or in another way of putting it, the single burning problem was how to let man travel out through space and back again safely, but in the course of pursuing that quest not only were the biomedical disciplines becoming oddly crossed but for the sake of any orderly investigation at all the problems had to be more neatly classified and the tasks and projects arising out of them needed specific lines in well defined directions.

This was a discovery learned only in examining the task and project papers themselves—and there were enough of them to be both confusing and bewildering again. In the aeromedical labyrinth at Holloman they were still divided broadly between the fields of space biology and biodynamics: the study of unusual environments on living creatures, and the study of mechanical stresses on living tissues. But they still fell across all the earlier types of medical research (and anthropological, ecological, other kinds) before the Space Age as such had been born.

Following that near-Aristotelian order every project was classified with a title as well a number. And it was the title that gave the really fascinating clues to what the busy investigators were up to as they conducted tests, compared data, wrote technical reports, labored over design and specification sheets, and dreamed up new kinds of test equipment.

Such titles as Biodynamics of Space Flight, Biophysics of Abrupt Deceleration, Subgravity Studies, Psychophysiology of Weightlessness, Radiation Hazards of Primary Cosmic Particles, Tolerance to Impact Runs, Tolerance to Aircraft Crash Forces, Biophysics of Escape, Human Factors of Space Flight, Environmental Control in Sealed Cabins.

There were manifold problems. For instance a spacecraft returning from its orbital wanderings had to meet terrific resistance as it came in contact with the dense air of the earthly envelope again. And how would the space crew tackle it? Should they come straight down so that the high G forces would be of relatively short duration? Or would a long glide path with moderate but long-duration G's be the better course? And between this Scylla and Charybdis how many G's could the human frame take anyway, and in what proportions? Already some animal runs on the Holloman long track (the first as early as 1954) had proved that the lower primates could live through a hundred G's of deceleration lasting some fractions of a second. Also accelerations of more than six G's for as long as three seconds—a more significant finding from the standpoint of manned spacecraft takeoff. But what of longer periods? Higher G's? Body positions?

So it seemed that every problem was related more or less to every other problem (cutting across the old frontiers again as these new frontiers imposingly reared themselves), all alike making for a tangle of complexity.

But still the science doctors were laying down their new tradition. And one of them, the great John Paul Stapp himself (who was already a luminous part of the tradition not only for his spectacular activities but for his original and salty witticisms) had summed up the job with a remark that continued to re-echo through the Laboratory's corridors by way of enlightening newcomers.

"For one factor is encouraging," he had said. "There are only two models—male and female—of the human body currently available. Thus with no prospects of a new design any findings in this research should at least provide permanent standards."

Research—that was the real activity. And in view of the kind of research going on (many more kinds than psychomotor tasks with chimpanzees) the most tantalizing questions concerned just what was being done, by what methods, with what additional strange equipment and devices. In other words how were the space scientists simulating the space environment conditions that were to lead to the answers to their problems?

One such device that was used almost daily and aroused curiosity by its very name was the Bopper.

"I'm going to put you in a slingshot and fire you from here to there," the colonel said to the airman. "If you don't stop—just keep on going!"

The colonel was teasing but his intention was serious. The airman sensed the teasing but was also serious.

In his GI fatigues, sleeves rolled up, jaws bulging with a protruding mouthpiece like any pugilist, instruments wired to his body here and there beneath wide web belts, the airman climbed upon a short section of bolted-down track and took his place in a chair that looked like a prison electric chair.

Various people strapped him into it, pulling at waist and chest belts until he was as trussed as someone indeed paying the final grim penalty. Other men stood alertly at the knobs of paneled instruments nearby. One small group fussed with tripod-held cameras. The colonel looked even more serious. The airman grinned a very small grin.

Somewhere a motor started whirring. The chair began sliding back along the short length of track, stretching its thick rubbery attached cables to what seemed like the breaking point. Loudly, a man began counting. The buzz of instruments could now be heard. Lights flickered and then raced along some of the panels.

"Fire!" shouted the man who had counted.

With the *clang* of a trip-lever the chair hurtled forward. It stopped with a jolt that tore at the straps. The body of the rider tried to surge farther, stopped, held fast, made a blur of motion leaving its residue only in clenched fists, upstanding hair, throbbing neck and throat muscles. For an endless instant the rider's face showed an intensity of rigid struggle.

Then it was over, men were hurrying to his side, loosening the straps, removing the mouthpiece, feeling for his pulse, using stethoscope and sphygmomanometer, measuring heart rate and blood pressure. The nearby panel instruments raced with lights and needles registering other reactions.

The colonel, holding the stethoscope, teased the airman softly again.

"So the slingshot worked—you did stop."

"But I sure *wanted* to keep going!"

They both grinned—the airman a bit tiredly. It was fun but he still knew the remarks were serious.

For the colonel was none other than Stapp himself, known as the "fastest man on earth" since his last and most memorable rocket sled ride. (A long while back by this time, December 1954.) The sled's 40,000 pounds of rocket thrust had sped him faster than a .45 calibre bullet, with no special clothing to protect him other than a plastic helmet and face visor. At that speed the sled had overtaken and passed a T-33 jet trainer pacing it overhead. The 632-mph peak velocity had been reached in five seconds. The windblast had built as high as 11,000 pounds per square foot, the deceleration rate of onset had equaled 600 G's per second, the jolting stop had matched that of an automobile driver crashing against a stone wall at 120 miles an hour.

So the colonel knew quite a lot about sled rides, abrupt impact, what they were doing now with the ungainly thing he had called a slingshot. As a matter of fact he had invented it.

As for the airman, he was Alton Yates; young, modest, apparently not very distinguished, just one of the chaps at the Laboratory doing his bit in the interests of science.

The "slingshot" was something different. Though not very impressive looking. Just a chair-sled on a section of track, bolted down to the concrete floor in one of the aeromedical buildings. Elastic shock cord and a motor winch drew the sled back into tension. A cock-and-release lever let it go. Ingeniously contrived brake pads stopped it at the end of the track. Also stopping its human catapult, throwing many times the weight of his body against the straps, building up G forces that measured human endurance against abrupt deceleration. It was the first device of its kind in the world, built to Stapp specifications by the Northrop Aircraft people. Once its name had been Crash Restraint Demonstrator, then Northrop Demonstration Decelerator, even Bungee Shock Cord Crash Force Simulator!

Not even the "fastest man on earth" could work with titles like that.

So the Bopper name had simplified things. And it had gone on with its slinging, often with dummies, more often with humans—as it was to hurtle them long after the colonel himself was gone. As a slingshot it was a veritable giant. But as a sled-and-track unit it could be called a midget. Especially the track. For instance compared with the famous 35,000-foot test track one had to lop off 34,980 feet just to match track lengths.

Yet the Bopper's modest twenty feet just exactly suited Bopper needs.

Man's race toward the stars with higher and higher flights and reentry problems had increasingly posed the G problem, and hitting into post-reentry shock or encountering land or water impact with space vehicles would be something like hitting the end of the Bopper track for tests of high-G heart and physical reactions.

The unit itself weighed about 800 pounds. Built mostly of aluminum alloy, with a 101-pound sled, a 36-pound chair cushioned in leather and foam rubber, a bungee-type cord and cable for its enormous rubber-band trigger tension, a brake wedge under the sled and fifteen consecutively acting pairs of spring-tensioned brake pads at the end of the track, it could be stopped in inches and produce as much as 30 G's depending on the exact shock cord tension and brake setting applied.

Moreover to be used as a scientific space tool it required a high degree of technical operation. Every one of its hundred performances a year had to be planned so as to have on hand a flight surgeon, an ambulance and hospital crew, the task scientist and his working crew, documentary photographers, an instrumentation crew of Land-Air technicians. (The Land-Air Corporation was Holloman's largest contractor group, whose over-all job was the entire missile range, a data-gathering agency supplying telemetry, tracking and recording equipment, camera crews, technical operators to collect the record without which the activities themselves would have been useless.)

At the Bopper site the Land-Air men instrumented the sled, adjusted the accelerometers or strain gauges, fitted the electrodes on the man who was to ride the sled. Their remarkable machines showed such results as time duration, number of G's on sled and subject, EKG data, velocity rates. Their oscillographs made permanent records for data reduction and their oscilloscopes showed acceleration and EKG graphs during the run. Their Fastax ribbon-frame cameras made a pictorial record at better than 1,600 frames a second for later visual study of every slow-motion aspect of the run.

"In fact without Land-Air," one of the task scientists, Lieutenant Dan Enfield, was fond of saying, "we'd be lost here."

This scientific and technical care was also noticeable in the work of the Bopper's firing chief, known as the brake-and-velocity control man.

It was the touchy responsibility of the firing chief to adjust every set of brake pads for the desired G force, double-check the settings with special gauges, calculate the seat position, the velocity tension, the rate of onset, supervise the strapping in of the subject, the placement of particular instruments—and do the actual firing.

"It's touchy because of the man riding," said the same Enfield. "Whoever sets the brakes shares the ride just in thinking of the possible mistakes."

Which posed another question with its tantalizing aspects; were all these people riding the Bopper because they liked it?

But let Alton Yates speak again—Yates who had ridden for Colonel Stapp and after all was surprisingly distinguished, having made the Bopper ride more than sixty times already, one of the few with that distinction.

"I ride the Bopper because it's exciting to be *doing* something," he said, a bit awkward about being asked to say anything. "But the other feelings don't change either. Like waiting for the countdown. And then just a little fear of the unknown every time."

He added that it was the fear which made the Bopper count seem like the longest countdown in the world.

Like every Bopper rider he also had the job of writing a subjective report of his reactions during each run, a shrewd touch added by the task scientists for truly empirical evidence. Most of the reports were as laconic as they were factual.

"I didn't feel anything significant this time," wrote Alfredo Martinez, "but about an hour later I noted a blister on the left arm where the electrode had contacted the skin."

"Upon impact I could feel sharp pains around the area of the left hip," wrote Yates himself. "The next morning there was no sign of pain."

"At impact my wind was partially knocked out," wrote task scientist Enfield. "There was a pulling pain below the right shoulder blade and pressing pain across the abdomen."

Of another run he reported: "Belt was adjusted comfortably tight with the buckle directly forward of left iliac crest. Impact was comparatively smooth and painless with noticeable duration. Wind only slightly affected."

"Experienced very little pain on or after impact," wrote Captain Jack Recht. "Slight discomfort in paralumbar muscles on both sides prior to run, probably due to shoulder straps. This discomfort became emphasized after impact. Headache, frontal region, persisting three or four hours."

A list of all the Bopper riders read almost like a roster of the Laboratory itself. Captain Dan Mosely, biodynamics chief, Lieutenant Colonel Rufus Hessberg who was now replacing Stapp, Captain DePaul Corkhill, task scientist Al Zaborowski. Catapulted on its low seat more times than most youngsters might have endured roller-coaster rides had been all the Lab's hard-working master and tech sergeants—Ed Dittmer and Roy Gatewood, Lee Pierce, James Ferguson, Howard Blackburn, Per Fahlstrom, Loren Bartrand, Al Wiedeman, Marion Rathbun, Tom Meidl, Nick Skames, Bob Bush, Gordon Wilson—but the list was endless.

Captain Eli Beeding, who had made the nation's headlines in one of his many Daisy rides (though in a way nobody would have dreamed of or expected), already had the record for a greater combined total of Daisy and Bopper rides behind his long lean frame than any man lean or otherwise.

Year by year the variety of Bopper projects, too, had increased. Also their sophisticated aspects. (There was a spectacular one involved with the Project Mercury astronauts when Eli Beeding rode the Bopper in full pressure suit and helmet, trailing a long hose like a giant umbilicus to maintain pressure and determine the helmet's effects on the neck's cervical vertebrae during impact—but the really spectacular part then was the name printed in bold letters across the bright orange space suit: astronaut WALTER SCHIRRA.)

Likewise the number of Bopper riders accumulated. New passenger-volunteers were turning up all the time and every one of them seemed to have heard about "Colonel Stapp's giant slingshot ride." The rides continued to be as short as ever. But a thought could be had even from that—perhaps a dreamer's thought, a space dreamer's long fancy. For couldn't one think of such rides extending straight into the future, bearing their special knowledges that would some day help to carry other passengers—alive—on their longer rides through space itself?

14

THE DAISY

From Sled to Lunar Landings

BUT THE BOPPER was not the only Stapp-inspired device the Laboratory owned to help the space doctors with their problems. There was also the Daisy track.

The Daisy—quaintly but simply named after the Daisy air rifle—was, at first, a pair of tubular-steel, well-oiled track rails five feet apart and 120 feet long upon which a pneumatic-powered sled fastened to the rails by metal slipper-rings was catapulted up to 100 miles an hour within 40 feet or less and stopped by a piston fixed to the front of the sled as it slid into a snug-fitting water-filled cylinder built like a huge abutment at the end of the rails. A plastic disc held the water in place until the piston hit it, and numerous holes in the cylinder walls could be individually stoppered to get the exactly decelerative G force planned for.

The variety of bodily positions and G loads in the Daisy programs had helped the Holloman researchers to answer some of the most burning questions as to how man can best survive the aerodynamic forces of space flight.

However, the story is a lot more interesting than that. One reason being John Paul Stapp himself.

I had first met him at the Bopper track and a few times thereafter among his many briefer returns to Holloman over the years, where he was apt to pop up at any time on aeromedical matters. A medium-built dark-haired bespectacled man of middle age with a mild way of talking and touches of grey at the temples, his appearance seemed to belie in every way the reputation he had gathered.

But part of that reputation was due both to his outspokenness and his wit—and both were frequently in evidence even when he was discharging his official duties.

For instance in his automotive crash studies—another program of vital interest to him which in fact had kept pace with his aerospace studies—he described people's indifference to seat belts as negligent suicide. Once at an automotive conference at Holloman I was as electrically amused as the rest of his large audience when he compared such belts to contraceptives and added: "For if either fails no money-back guarantee is going to do the slightest good." There was also the time when a piece of mistaken news had gotten out to the public telling of barnyard pigs instead of bears riding on the Daisy track—which he neatly skewered with a headline that became a classic: "Pig Tale Disproved by 'Bear' Facts." And when a Congressional committee questioned him about why hogs and chimpanzees were used in the strange doings at Holloman another classic reply had been born: "You wonder why? Well, man is somewhere between the hog and the chimpanzee—some are more like hogs and others more like chimpanzees."

But this was the amusing John Paul Stapp—there was his other more serious side. The side that had brought him from a childhood in Brazil with his missionary parents to school and college in the United States, through zoology and chemistry and medical studies to become a regular doctor, then an aviation medicine graduate and flight surgeon, a biophysicist in research at several aeromedical centers, a practical experimenter taking high-altitude open-canopy flights to test such things as windblast and liquid-oxygen breathing systems, a rocket sled rider first at Edwards Air Force Base and then at Holloman—and a man who had collected along the way of these not-academic studies some battering of the physical economy, including sundry arm and rib fractures, retinal hemorrhages, mild concussions, innumerable bumps and pains and bruises, all in the quiet pursuit of an interior philosophy unlike that of the ancient Greek philosophers—who had submitted nothing to experiment.

For these things he had received national honors. The Legion of Merit, the Air Force's Cheney Award, the Aeronautical Science Institute Award, the National Air Council Award, more than a score of others. Also, an honorary Doctor of Science degree from his alma mater, Baylor University—in the same ceremony with another rather well-known recipient, President Dwight D. Eisenhower.

Also notoriety. Television appearances, a "This Is Your Life" appearance, a Twentieth Century Fox movie filmed at Holloman, the Stapp portrait done by Artzibasheff for the cover of Time Magazine, articles in Collier's, Reader's Digest, other periodicals.

It was this quiet man who sat in a corner of a Holloman building one late-spring day in 1963 just as quietly telling me the true history of the Daisy track, long after I had watched its performances and become familiar with the many Holloman activities. Nothing in his bearing hinted at such impressive past experiences. As deputy chief scientist of the Aerospace Medical Division at Brooks Air Force Base, Texas (another research center of the Air Force Systems Command), he had appeared once more at Holloman, this time for one of its latest programs, a really far-out program, requested by the National Aeronautics and Space Administration for its Project Apollo moon landings, whose potential capsule impacts had just been studied in every possible configuration on this same modest Daisy track.

"The Daisy was born May 13, 1953," he told me, peering mildly through his glasses and pausing until I had it written. "At any rate that was the date I wrote the Disposition Form describing it in detail. In that original concept two pistons and cylinders were planned, also various ranges of abruptness, magnitude, duration, ranging from two hundred G's down to five, and for impact one-tenth of a second maximum."

Seated on a high stool like a classroom lecturer, in a cluttered instrument room not far from the track, he described further technical features and continued: "From these designs the contractor built the track, water brake, and sled, finishing in 1955, though for cost reasons the pneumatic catapult was postponed and instead ejection seat catapults were used to propel the sled during the next five years."

Like an afterthought he added: "Nevertheless the track was christened the Daisy in honor of the Daisy air rifle long before it was built."

For a moment he seemed to meditate. "From its earliest proof runs the track lived up to all its design objectives," he went on with a faintly reminiscent and satisfied air. "One of these was low operating costs compared to sleds propelled by rockets on large tracks—and I might add," he said, showing the shadowy ghost of a different Stapp expression, "the cost of the ejection seat catapults was less than five percent that of JATO rockets, while the cost of desert air compressed by an electric motor stayed at less than five cents per run."

Still ensconced on the stool he peered down at me through eyelids showing tiny red networks of lines at the outside corners; mute testimony to what windblast and rocket sled rides had done.

"The total number of Daisy runs has now reached fifteen hundred," he remarked. "Which is one reason I telephoned you—it's an interesting number."

While I thought of that (and wrote) he went off once more into precise technical descriptions, this time of the several Daisy sleds that had already seen their better days only to be replaced by more sophisti-

cated versions—the latest "omnidirectional" type being a far cry indeed from the backward-forward-upright sled Eli Beeding had once
ridden into national news headlines.

"This omnidirectional type is the ultimate," he stated, and described
it minutely for me. "First there's the large steel ring mounted laterally
on the sled bed. Diametrically across the ring is the long oval frame,
and mounted on gimbals across the middle of the frame is the seat. The
frame can be clamped in any horizontal angle around the circle formed
by the ring. The frame is held between the gimbals on the clamps
securing it to the ring. The gimbals permit the frame to be tilted at any
angle toward left or right of the subject in the seat. The gimbal-mounted
seat inside the frame can be tipped forward or backward to any selected
angle in the subject's vertical plane. So you see the subject can be locked
in place in any combination of roll from zero to three hundred and
sixty degrees, pitch from zero to one hundred eighty degrees, and yaw
from zero to one hundred eighty degrees. For instance when NASA
wanted to find out through these present tests the human tolerances
and optimum restraints for the three astronauts in an Apollo moon-
flight capsule during parachute landings on desert ground, all possible
angles of impact had to be tested simulating those of the Apollo
landings."

I wrote madly, and he waited. I thought it was over. But the heart of
the matter had not even been mentioned.

"We rode our human subjects to cover an impact velocity range from
twenty to forty-five feet per second," he continued with the same quiet
care, like one cherishing his subject or the gratifying results attained
from it, "and our anaesthetized animals and dummy subjects up to a
hundred and fifty feet a second. Impact durations were forty to a hundred milliseconds. Peak G forces ranged from ten to thirty-six G's for
our human volunteers and up to a hundred and seventy G's on animals
and dummies. The rates of impact varied from five hundred to two
thousand G's per second for humans and on up to ten thousand G's per
second for animals. One human experiment at a thousand G's per second with a twenty-five-G peak resulted from hitting the water cylinder
brake at thirty-two feet per second and stopping in less than sixteen
inches in five-hundredths of a second. The runs also covered eight different positions around the circle with the seat upright and tipped forward forty-five degrees then backward forty-five degrees, using two subjects for each configuration."

He slid from the stool and began pacing a little, wearing the reminiscent smile again. I suspected something different coming.

"I might add that our human subjects seemed to find the sample blood-drawing more objectionable than the sled impacts," he remarked drily. "Except for Sergeant Tourville who sustained the most painful impact, a compression injury of the soft tissues in the area of the seventh, eighth, and ninth thoracic vertebrae. To describe it a bit more thoroughly, he gasped with pain and couldn't breathe for a while in the seat. Later we X-rayed him and found no intervertebral injuries, fractures, or other lasting effects. In fact he said he was glad if that particular run had helped locate something—and it did, for since our anthropomorphic dummy in the same type run made not the slightest complaint we would never have known a back injury could be caused by that type of impact. Later the NASA engineers came up with a new modification to attenuate the force in such a position. So you might say in summary—" he peered down at me and it was like all the John Paul Stapps at once speaking—"at the cost of a few stiff backs, kinked necks, bruised elbows, and occasional profanity the Apollo capsule has been made safe for the three astronauts who will have perils enough and left over in the unknown hazards of the first flight to the moon."

I felt that it was one of the most unusual interviews I had had at Holloman and said so. He seemed pleased. Later we talked of the Daisy performances of the past and then of the most memorable Daisy run of all, that of Eli Beeding taking his unprecedented number of G's and lapsing slowly into shock at the end. He was surprised that I remembered it.

But I had been there.

15

CRASH FORCES

What Happens in a Split-second Stop

PHYSIOLOGICALLY WHAT HAPPENED in the famous run was a mystery. Nor in a physiological sense has it been cleared up yet.

It was another bright near-summer day when Eli Beeding, as lean and handsome as a Hollywood candidate, climbed into the Daisy sled's heavily padded low seat with its high back-and-headrest to submit himself to some of the impacts he had been testing with more than thirty other subjects in a long series of runs to determine the limits of human tolerance to G forces.

Twenty-nine years of age and a Baylor graduate like his mentor Stapp, with an MA degree in physiology, a tour in Korea and half a dozen years of aeromedical experience behind him, Eli Lackland Beeding (often "Lack" to his friends) was definitely no playboy in the science field despite his sunny ways and handsome exterior. As assistant biodynamics chief at the Laboratory he was also task scientist for the present project. Which was one reason he was in the sled; hardly any project involving human hazards or volunteers was ever carried out without its leaders actively taking part. (Such was the Air Force way.)

The short high-railed track was located at one side of the few buildings known as the Vivarium, the original aeromedical site where Stapp's own office had been, long before chimpanzee colonies and the spillover to additional quarters a mile away. As one part of the nearest building a blockhouse had been tacked on—actually just a small many-windowed bay crowded with a modest array of electronic equipment such as velocity counters, oscillographs, and tape recorders, with intercom sets for sled and trackside communication and a PA system to control the countdown.

Other people besides Beeding were there that day, mostly project people. The biodynamics chief, Captain Dan Mosely, was supervising. Lieutenant Al Zaborowski was handling the countdown check list. Flight surgeon Captain Les Eason from the base hospital was conspicuous with his dangling stethoscope; hospital corpsmen also were there with an ambulance. The track mechanics headed by Pop Shields were busy seating the subject just so, adjusting his mouthpiece, strapping him into the backward-facing upright position selected for this run (of terrible significance as it later turned out). The Land-Air crew, Al Brown, Mac Connell, Roger Black, Ed Trout, others—the same men handling the Bopper runs so magnificently—were perhaps the busiest, calibrating the sled and chest accelerometers, installing the junction boxes, checking the whip cable with its trailing wires that tied into another junction box and then directly into the blockhouse instrumentation.

Another on hand was Harald von Beckh, the Laboratory's German-born subgravity scientist, with an anti-G platform designed to position a body automatically to transverse G forces, the kind easiest to endure. While others worked he too worked, installing the accelerometers that would measure longitudinal and transverse G forces and the potentiometer that would record the rotary movement of the platform.

With that over he began strapping in place the two small passengers the sled was also to carry—fully anesthetized, wire-netted Albino rats.

(This was known as free-loading, a non-interference task, with the test animal adjusted to move in any axis and the control animal to take the brunt of the test.)

The sled was Daisy Model Number Two, a 2,000-pound chromium-molybdenum steel structure propelled by an M1A1 (seat ejection type) catapult and designed to hold the seat between locking gimbals adjustable for any forward or backward facing angle within a 180-degree arc.

The run itself was number 335—routine in the series, except perhaps that it was the last in a progressive number with increased G's planned for each run. The forty or more runs of the Beeding series had already shown that at peak deceleration more G's were absorbed across the chest of the subject than on the sled itself, roughly in a ratio of three to two. This also bore out some earlier runs. For example in programming for 15 G's on the sled in this backward facing position the accelerometers had recorded about 22 G's across the chest; 20 G's on the sled had produced 30 on the chest; 30 sled G's had produced 45 on the chest.

Run number 335 was programmed for 40 G's on the sled—and therefore an expected 60 G's on the subject. (With a definite rate of onset and no more than a tenth of a second duration.)

But it didn't quite work out that way.

Everything was now ready—catapult installed (to kick the sled off), subject strapped, sled area cleared, the small knot of medical people and technicians clustered near the track end waiting as usual for instant re-examination of the sled occupant. In the bright afternoon sunshine Passenger 335 sat placidly, hands folded in his lap, head against the back rest, showing an easy and relaxed profile like that of a person who had been there before—as indeed Eli Beeding had.

In the blockhouse Zaborowski was intoning the countdown and technicians seemed to be studying the cabinet instruments.

The instant came. "Fire!"

With a muffled bang and a perfection of smooth action the sled rocketed from its starting place, gathering momentum, sliding on its rails, aiming its long piston at the black cannon-barrel cylinder hole—and with a thud found its target. Instantly it stopped, jolted, the rider's mouthpiece suddenly bared itself like a snarl, the head plunged into the backrest, the body strained upward and backward (in its backward position), then slowly slumped down again. For a long second the bared mouthpiece still produced the effect of a snarl. Pain or shock was a visible imprint on the face. But already the waiting group were racing toward the sled. And already on some faces showed a look of alarm.

In almost no time straps and instruments were loosed, coverall unbuttoned, shirt thrust back and stethoscope applied. The subject's head slumped lower; all the color had drained from his face. Someone removed the mouthpiece; someone else was fingering the accelerometer. The small instrument with its tension-wire would be the real tell-tale.

There was a blur of talk.

"What happened?"

"How is he, Doc?"

"Give him room there—he's got to breathe."

"I'm hurting." It was a small and languid remark, with a tired smile, almost like a joking effort. The examination went on.

"Where is the pain, Lack?"

"Spine." He smiled tiredly again. "But it's going numb, I feel dizzy now . . ."

Great drops of sweat stood out all over his forehead. His pallor deepened.

"Oh Lord, his back—!"

"We can't move him."

"Bring me that sphygmomanometer."

(It was an aneroid type, for easier reading.)

"How are you now, Eli?"

"I can't see too well. I think . . ." His voice trailed off.

"I can't get any blood pressure reading!" The flight surgeon's voice climbed with new worry, he wrapped up his pressure bandage. "We'll have to try moving him. Do you think you can walk, old man?"

"I don't—know. I think I'm—blacking out now . . ."

His head slumped all the way down.

"He's going into shock." The flight surgeon spoke quietly. "Help me with him."

Everyone tried to. Gently the inert body was lifted from the seat, eased down along the side of the sled floor, leaving the feet high in the air. Some of the blockhouse crew had hurried out. The accelerometer was mentioned again. Someone asked if the CEC readings had been gotten yet. (The oscillograph record that would really tell the tale.)

Slowly he came to . . . the eyes opened, looked dizzily around, the tired smile tried to manifest itself. He murmured.

"My back's still numb . . . what a bore. Can't we get out of here?"

"Move him inside," said Mosely (looking just as worried). "At least to the X-ray room."

The ambulance crew had a stretcher ready. Working carefully but expertly they accomplished what had to be done. Inside the building (one of those which had been noisy all morning with chimp preparations and the usual bedlam) the X-ray room was quiet and empty. Just as efficiently the stretcher crew slid their burden on to the long metal table, tilting the table so that his feet were again sloping upward. Every light in the place was turned on.

With a rush and a flurry one of the Land-Air instrument men appeared. His face was a study in consternation.

"It just *can't be!*" He thrust out his scroll of photosensitive paper, showing its long wavy scrawls. "*Eighty-three G's!*"

"Oh my Lord," Mosely said. "On the chest accelerometer?"

"On the chest accelerometer. But it *can't* be. The sled reading is still forty G's—exactly as programmed!"

Another Land-Air man had followed. "We're just not getting the right readings," he muttered. But his expression was just as bewildered; certain of nothing. More people came in. There was a babel of talk.

"Did you hear that, Eli—do you know the G load you took?"

The tired face smiled. "I heard. But who believes it?" He arched his back and groaned slightly.

The accelerometer was a subject of new hot debate. Increasing bewilderment. It had been like a quantum jump. More instrument people came in, the record was gone over again, comparing its other tell-tale signs—rate of onset 5,000 G's per second—peak duration one tenth of a second . . .

And if it were really true—for that brief fraction of time the body of a man had absorbed a force equal to 11,620 pounds, *83 times its actual weight*, yet here was the man, shaken and white and dizzy but not only still alive, still able to smile!

"Maybe it is true," someone murmured.

And then Captain Dan Mosely paused, stiffened, and a look of horror overspread his face.

"Oh Lord," he whispered again. "Lack, if you'd been seated *facing forward—!*"

As the thought sank in, others who knew what that meant began to have the same look. Nevertheless the Beeding smile, wry and cautious, still glimmered up at all of them.

"You'll admit," he murmured, "it's at least proved *this* position."

At the base hospital where he was taken later that afternoon for more X-rays and a fuller checkup it was found that Captain Eli Beeding needed two days' treatment with his feet in traction for sore vertebrac, also a few doses of barbiturates for intermittent pain, after which the traumatic experience cleared up and on the third day he was freed for normal duty again. But in the meantime other things had been happening.

The mystery of the unexpected G load had created an understandable flurry in the Laboratory. The very day following the run saw the Daisy track busy again, this time with the use of two anaesthetized bears. (An animal with a spinal configuration very similar to that of man.) A run was made with each, seated in the same backward-facing position, programmed exactly the same, for 40 G's on the sled and 60 (expected) across the chest. In each case the result was 80 G's across the chest. (Though neither animal showed any other unusual effects.)

So it seemed that the quantum jump had indeed taken place—as mysterious in gravity forces as in physics, but at least one G plateau reached. Nor did later runs in that and other positions and with other subjects and types of subjects show up any differently. The programming for as high as a 35-G sled load always produced the 3:2 ratio of the "formula"—but programming for 40 G's on the sled simply doubled the chest load. This was something about the G phenomenon that certainly needed further investigating—and again the problems for the space doctors were multiplying!

Nevertheless, as Beeding himself had said, the problem of a man tolerating 83 G's of force for a fraction of a second in a backward-facing position had unquestionably been proved—and in showing the limits of human tolerance to G forces it had even accomplished the test objective. It had also proved that the backward-facing position was the best for absorbing high crash forces, in an aircraft or any other vehicle. Which could be of interest even to vehicle manufacturers. Even for space vehicles.

But the aeromedical flurry had not been the only kind generated, nor perhaps even the biggest. For still other things had been happening.

Again it was on the day following the famous run, while he still reclined in a hospital bed temporarily suspended in pulley-weights, that the Eli Beeding name became the source of excitement in another way. He became news.

The story had been sent out through the wire services and other news media after quick discussion in the Holloman office and with higher headquarters, and immediately it had started. By the time the queries were beginning to flood in, the news had scored among the top ten items of the day in New Mexico—and before the day was out the same news was among the national top ten.

The visitors started coming. Mostly press people, newspaper and radio and local TV, but also scientific visitors, space medicine people who had heard about the event and wanted more of its clinical details. The press people were mostly received in the information office but the aeromedical people who appeared from time to time were of course immediately *persona grata* at the Laboratory itself.

As time went on there was also official appreciation. A Legion of Merit award, with the appropriate ceremonies. Invitations to panel discussions, professional addresses at Aerospace Medical Association meetings.

By the time the event itself was aeromedical history Eli Beeding also might conceivably have had enough of it. But as he went about his normal duties in the biodynamics section no one would have known that. Once, long after the event, I got him to describe his actual feelings and sensations of that day. We sat in his office in one of the newer aeromedical buildings, with the eternal southwest sunshine spilling its light as brilliantly as ever through the windows.

"The first thing I felt was the spinal pain." (He spoke with the tone of one at last reminiscing far back.) "As if a baseball bat had been applied to the bottom of the back. Then there was the numbness and dizziness, I couldn't feel my back at all. I kept trying to talk, I wanted to tell them what was happening to me, but then I sensed my vision beginning to go. I could hear the talking around me, about the blood pressure for instance, just no pressure at all, zero zero. But there was too much dizziness and then I knew I was actually going to pass out. I think that's the last thing I did tell them."

As I sat listening I was also in line-of-sight with a large framed and glassed wall-board: an odd homemade display with heavy title-lettering which read "500 G Club." Below the lettering a half-dozen postcard-sized photos were spotted, of men riding the Daisy or the Bopper sled; those who at that time had already endured a total of 500 G's or more in the course of their accumulated volunteer rides. Alton Yates was one, Alfredo Martinez another, Ellis Taylor another, James Ferguson another—and Eli Beeding in the same picture at the peak of his most unusual Daisy ride which by now had become familiar even as a news picture.

While we were still talking he happened to think of something else. "Do you remember Harald von Beckh's rats on the sled?"

My face must have looked as foolish as I felt—not only had they been forgotten but even getting the story had been lost sight of completely.

I made the obvious query. "What happened to them?"

The 83-G Daisy rider chuckled and made a sly Paul Newman grin.

"They didn't even go into shock," he said.

16

MULTIGRAVITY

Spirals and Parabolas Into the Future

As for Harald von Beckh, there was the time I found him on the Holloman flight line and wondered exactly what he was doing there in the burning noonday sun.

In shirt-sleeves and casual civilian clothes, he was talking at length with two others in flight togs, an officer and an airman, at the foot of an F-94C cockpit ladder.

He had invited me there—after a good many previous meetings about rats and other things—and I listened. He sounded instructive in what he was saying. Over his shoulder I examined the three small sketches, full of corkscrew lines and long curves, which he was showing while he traced out certain flight patterns.

"You see, Captain—here the diagram shows us. First just with the G spirals, then straight and level flight. But then here—from twenty-five thousand feet the spirals down to fifteen thousand, then full thrust and the ascending parabola. There should be at least six G's from acceleration. Then forty seconds subgravity in the upward arc."

The captain nodded. His own remarks made it clear that he had been flying such missions for weeks, always with varying instructions. Wide-shouldered and serious-faced, laced tightly into his dark brown anti-G suit, he looked as dependable as a rock.

"Then the reverse pattern. See here again. Afterburner on, full thrust up to thirty-three thousand feet, same subgravity. Then here you have four hundred knots at parabola end. This should be followed by thirty-second spirals."

Their heads leaned together over the small sketches. The slender young airman, third of the trio, studied as intently, only turning when one of the aircraft's ground crew came forward to strap him in a leather harness which held two small accelerometers tightly against his chest. In the brilliant sunshine his pale freckles stood out as sharply as his sand-colored crew-cut, making him look very boyish.

From the top of the ladder the crew chief was giving the aircraft its final check. Both cockpit places had been fitted with certain special instruments. As he came down, the captain and his young airman-passenger put on their helmets, tested their oxygen masks, began climbing upward.

The tightly laced G suit, the round polished helmets, the bulbous masks might have seemed the garb of men from Mars, once. Now they were familiar additions to modern and experimental flight. Beneath the raised canopy of the trim Lockheed with its powerful Pratt-Whitney turbojet engine they adjusted themselves tandemwise in their narrow seats, pushed the masks aside again as von Beckh followed them up the ladder. He seemed intent on his own checks.

"So—clock and accelerometer in position for the pictures. Good. And the oscillograph here, for the chest accelerometer. The camera points well. Now you know how to react, when to relax—" he spoke to the airman, volunteer for today's experiment. "You know when to remove your mask—be sure it goes to one side, your face must be quite clear this time for the camera. Anyway, you already know."

He spoke as if to calm the other for the physical stress and mental concentration of the coming flight.

And Airman Cecil Layton looked calm. Like the pilot, Captain Arthur Miller, he had been on many such flights. Ever since Doctor Harald von Beckh had arrived at the aeromedical lab to take over such projects.

Now von Beckh was inspecting the 16mm camera. In its metal casing near the shiny oblong-boxed oscillograph, ready for instant switch-on in flight, it pointed its long-barreled lens like a gun at the airman's head. Von Beckh looked pleased. He slid along the ladder and peered into the front cockpit. At the improved accelerometer. The G meter. The vertical-horizontal micro-ammeters (designed by the previous subgravity task scientist, Captain Grover Schock).

"Next week we fly our new galvanic skin-response meter." He suddenly had to shout as a high screeching jet blast along the flight line muffled other sounds. "And later an instrument to record the action potential of muscles."

As the jet blast began simmering off he smiled at the pilot, touched his shoulder. "But today the three parabolas and the same experiment, yes?"

The captain smiled back. Perhaps because von Beckh was a pilot also, who had flown many of the present missions. Carefully they went over the flight patterns again. Just two pilots "talking shop." But shop talk involving the weirdest conditions man had yet encountered in his flights farther and farther along the vertical frontier. Multigravity conditions, and subgravity or zero-gravity conditions.

Multigravity, building up G forces that loaded the body with weight and drained the brain of blood, producing blackout and unconsciousness. And its fantastic opposite, the phenomenon of subgravity or weightlessness, causing the body to lose its normal one-G load and float without solid sensations in the mystery called space.

For these were the objectives of today's experiments. To simulate such conditions deliberately. To induce high G by high acceleration through tight-flying spirals that would accumulate centrifugal force. And to induce zero G by parabolic arcs or Keplerian trajectories in which centrifugal force would exactly equal gravity pull while engine thrust exactly counterbalanced air friction.

Why?

The answer was simpler than some of the experiments. To solve some of the weightiest problems (no pun intended!) of travel through space. To find man's physical limits and to find ways of overcoming or extending those limits through mechanics, aerodynamics, physics, biophysics, all the sciences—and through the adaptability of man himself. In short, to find how man himself could survive in space

All this was behind the talk at the cockpit ladder—and other things too, as I had found. For instance the fact that these very combinations of high-G and zero-G flying patterns had been von Beckh's own unique contribution to space biology research. By including the spirals with the parabolas he had discovered some curious further stresses a man would have to contend with physically. Also by reversing and mixing the arcs and spirals and by timing them against leveling-off pull-outs. For instance learning that by starting with G-building spirals and then going into the parabolas it definitely caused slower recovery from blackout.

Some of his findings, published in 1952, had stolen a march on another band of experimenters whose world-famous orbiting dog Laika (in 1957) showed the same lag in recovery from acceleration.

Which was not the first time von Beckh had scooped the field in space biology research. Vienna-born, glider pilot and regular pilot, medical doctor, Luftwaffe flight surgeon, teacher in Berlin's Air Force Medical Academy, he had been lucky enough to become associated with the small group of German scientists who from the early 1930's until the end of the war were the leaders in aviation medicine in Europe.

Inspired by such men as Heinz von Diringshofen and Hubertus Strughold (the man often called the father of aviation medicine) he had begun experimenting in Stuka dive bombers for multi-G and zero-G studies even then—and it was the same inspiration which kept him pioneering after the war.

For after the war there had been a small band of them, scattered through the Western world, some together, some alone, some civilian, some military, yet space doctors all, working independently or in groups, analyzing and testing, trying out animals and themselves, pooling their findings; a select band among the very forerunners of the new age of space medicine and space flight. Though not in Germany of course. There, even aviation medicine had stopped. And so the German element had gone farther afield. Some to other European countries, many to the United States, many to Argentina. Harald von Beckh had gone to Argentina.

In Buenos Aires he first went into private medical practice as a licensed M.D. But he had not lost sight of aeromedical research, his real passion. So it happened that after a while he became a professor-lecturer at the *Instituto Nacional de Medicina Aeronautica*—and went on with his experimenting.

This time with *Hydromedusa tectifera*. (Really only water turtles!) But the first actual experiments of their kind: using animals in aircraft for space research. Flying them and himself through countless vertical dives and parabolic flights in a two-seater Fiat fighter plane supplied by the Argentine Air Force.

So the turtles had taught him something too. For instance about disturbed physical orientation, the slacking off of neuro-muscular co-ordination, labyrinthine malfunctions, normal and abnormal G reactions. Carried aloft in water-filled glass containers, the small reptilian beasts, noted for their rapacity as well as their speed and skill underwater in striking like a snake with pinpoint accuracy, had been offered bits of meat every time the flight produced subgravity or zero-gravity conditions. But in the weightless state it was found that Hydromedusa repeatedly struck under, over, to one side of the bait, until newly oriented by numerous such flights. Actually the experiments were far more complicated, involving various disorientation methods, with and without labyrinthine functions, also equilibrium and vision and kinesthetic sense studies, and exhaustive flight tests of all descriptions.

After that von Beckh published a paper about it. And found his first touch of fame.

The paper, "Experiments with Animal and Human Subjects Under Sub- and Zero-Gravity Conditions During the Dive and Parabolic Flight," was printed and reprinted through the aerospace medicine world, in Switzerland by the International Astronautical Congress, in Latin America by *Revista Nacional de Aeronautica*, in the United States by the *Journal of Aviation Medicine*.

Meanwhile at Holloman, long before he got there himself, certain others in that select band had been doing their own experimenting— J. P. Henry, Stapp, Simons, Schock—for instance with the V-2 and Aerobee-Hi mice and monkeys, and also correlating their findings. Presently Stapp and von Beckh were writing to each other. Which accounted for the fact that von Beckh was at Holloman now and had taken over the subgravity flights from Grover Schock—in itself an interesting transition.

For it was but one more example of how the little band all over the space flight world were delving into the same problems and coming up with this or that part of the complex answers. In 1955 Schock had started the F-94C subgravity flights, using himself as a subject. But now he too was undertaking new experiments, notably in underwater gravity studies and in the psychology of zero-G exposure.

And now von Beckh was extending the F-94C flight ideas. Once he had told me that this Lockheed aircraft with its J-48-P-7 engine and afterburner which could develop 8,750 pounds of thrust was aerodynamically the best for producing the unique condition called weightlessness. The trick of balancing centrifugal force and gravity pull (plus other factors) apparently was not too easy even with an expert pilot. The F-94C made it more likely because of pilot skill combined with the characteristics of the aircraft itself.

But at any rate here he stood on the Holloman flight line, still talking shop—going over the technique now for the arcs and spirals wanted.

". . . So remember, Captain, don't make the accelerations too prolonged. Not over thirty seconds. But give the subject continuous high load. If you start at four G's and go to five, then go into weightlessness as quickly as possible."

Once again the pilot nodded. Actually the high G results were the easiest part. (If anything was easy about it!) By flying his spirals at full thrust through 10,000-foot drops they sometimes built up to five or six G's or even more, depending on initial thrust and the radius of the spiral.

Yet even the techniques were improving. On rare occasions there would be seven G's, as much as 45 seconds of weightlessness. True, there were frustrations—watches and cameras might stop, tape recorders fail to work. But 51 successful flights and over 200 parabolas had been accomplished, using different pilots and many volunteers, which improved the statistical result. Now these results too were beginning to shape up.

Though that word *beginning* had to be emphasized too. During one of our previous meetings (in the von Beckh office crammed with books, papers, notes) I had asked him to spell out at least some of those objectives and results. And as he paced the floor, sat, got up again, pulled out dozens of written or printed examples and smoked innumerable cigarettes, he had assented.

"We've been simulating as nearly as possible the conditions of rocket ascent and reentry for manned orbital and space flight. By pullouts and tight diving spirals we expose the subject to positive accelerations for the desired G level. By giving up altitude we sustain the level. In some cases we find this produces marked gray-out. Then the weightless state comes with the Keplerian ballistic trajectories. We've combined these patterns by pre-weightless acceleration simulating rocket thrust and then weightlessness following burnout by dive-and-spiraling for about forty seconds to a minute and then going into a subgravity trajectory. On the other hand the post-weightless accelerations simulating reentry we get by flying the parabola first and then the diving spiral. Another thing we've found is that almost every subject experiences higher strain when exposed to the G load immediately after a weightless state."

He paced and thought some more. "Oh yes, and there's this. We've also been probing the psychological conditions here. With radio communication from the ground we ask test questions and compare one man's response with another. For instance in word associating, inverted number repeating, syllable completion, also by simple picture-drawing tests. In these fifty-one missions we've been measuring these responses and finding some noticeably different. But it's too early to draw all the conclusions yet. All our subjects have been flying in conventional sitting positions in conventional aircraft. Much more has to be done about supine positions and other means of protecting the astronaut against all these conditions."

This had reminded me of the rats again and I asked about that.

"Oh yes, the rats—and the anti-G platform." At once he brought down from a high shelf a metal model of the platform and proceeded to explain it in detail. "This illustrates the principle of an anti-G device. For instance it's known that maximum G tolerance is at right angles to the long axis of the body. So you see when this platform pivots about the lateral axis of the aircraft or space vehicle it's through the action of acceleration itself that it assumes a position perpendicular to the heart-head line of the body and therefore changes longitudinal G's into more easily tolerated transverse G's. In other words it avoids the action of significant parallel-to-spine loads. For instance when Captain Beeding endured those eighty-three G's—" (I had particularly asked him about that run)—"the animals I had on the sled then showed this. The unprotected or control animal received noticeable internal effects by taking the G load in the vulnerable longitudinal axis. The animal on the anti-G platform took the load in the less critical transverse position—in which four or five times as much deceleration can be endured."

. . . So I had found that all this too was behind the affair of the casually dressed von Beckh giving out his flight instructions on a cockpit ladder on the sun-drenched Holloman flight line.

Yet most of it went still farther back into the past. In a sense all the way back to those first early days with Hubertus Strughold and the Stuka dive bombers—just as it was destined, crystal ball or no, to go forward into manned space flight and the orbital spacecraft itself.

Or as he had explained it to me: those first Stuka experiments had been a part of the first days of aviation medicine itself, and in those days the first aeromedical laboratory had been the aircraft itself. Only later had come the mechanical gadgets, the centrifuges, the cockpit mockups, the hyper-ventilation respirators, the ground chambers and capsules. All wonderful for theory and for a mass of experimentation, but still not enough for the final answers, for instance this probe into pure weightlessness now. For here again was an experiment that couldn't be simulated with any known ground equipment. And thus the two bulkily clad, oddly instrumented figures sat once more in the "original laboratory," the aircraft, helping the man who was the task scientist find out what man had to know.

He had finished his instructions at last and was climbing down from the cockpit ladder. We stood on the cement apron together as he waved at both pilot and passenger, smiled genially, held up one hand making a ring of thumb and forefinger in the traditional flying salute, while they grinned back and did the same. The sudden high-pitched jet engine whine as the crew chief gave his own signal drowned out the final friendly words and almost seemed to drown one's thoughts again.

Yet all at once it was clear, in that thunderous takeoff, while von Beckh still waved and shaded his eyes, what he had really been doing there in the noonday sun.

17

SUBGRAVITY

Space Frogmen Into the Past

THE SUBJECT OF GRAVITY still intrigued me. And in devouring all the available space books I had again come across the quaint story of that greatest of the early Greek scientists, Archimedes, as he sat in his bath one day discovering that "a body immersed in fluid loses as much weight as that of the fluid it disperses." After which he immediately jumped out (so the story goes) and ran naked down the street shouting: "Eureka! I have found it!"

What he had found, of course, was one of the first known or formulated principles concerning that most mysterious of phenomena, gravity itself.

There were other stories just as interesting.

When Galileo, medieval Italy's foremost astronomer and physicist, worked Archimedes' hydrostatic theories into a better formula, dropped objects from Pisa's leaning tower to prove the weightlessness of falling bodies, and at last, like Copernicus, declared that the earth itself moved and was round, the Inquisition made him recant his theories but (so the story goes) he made his *sotto voce* whisper: "Just the same the earth does move!"

Galileo's many findings went a tremendous way in the study of gravity.

And when Sir Isaac Newton, that giant among physicists, who happened to get himself born the very year Galileo died, went on reflecting about these same mysteries and then formulated the theory of gravity itself, he rubbed his head ruefully where a falling apple (so the story goes) had bumped his thoughts into profounder discoveries.

Though it may be no far cry intellectually from Archimedes to Galileo to Newton, Titans all who dominated their ages, it might seem too far from them to a young American scientist standing completely submerged in a modern swimming pool, directing other men in certain experiments newly concerned with those first great discoveries.

Still, there were a few similarities.

In fact Grover J. D. Schock, Air Force captain and aerospace scientist, not only knew his Archimedean and Galilean and Newtonian principles. In his simple aqualung, gripping iron weights to keep his subaqueous position, he was quietly investigating theories they would have been interested in themselves had they lived in the modern Space Age. He was trying to find out if a body separated or partly separated from its normal weight or gravity force was also separated from its normal sense perceptions—and if so, how and why.

He was trying this because it meant practically everything for human bodies traveling from earth into space. He was using the knowledge from his illustrious predecessors as major links in the experimental chain —just as all science, music, art, thought itself has been used since the written record began. Archimedes' shrewd facts about displacement were in it. So were Galileo's notions about falling bodies. Newton's laws and principles were like prime movers.

He was also using newer ideas. For instance a contemporary scientist, Margaria, had furnished the modern idea of underwater experimentation, the "simulation of subgravity conditions by immersion of a body in a fluid having the same specific gravity as that of the body"—and wasn't that old Archimedes all over again?

Another similarity was the laboratory method, the true way of science, the Baconian way. (And the aircraft laboratory way?) Francis Bacon had been one of the first of such empirical scientists, in fact had died that way, when he caught pneumonia while trying to prove that a frozen chicken wouldn't decompose. Now the laboratory was only a swimming pool, as ordinary an environment as a bathtub, or for that matter a bit of earth under an apple tree. But a laboratory because water and its own peculiar properties produced a sensory-starved environment—which was exactly the thing needed for the present experiments.

But perhaps the closest link between the young Air Force scientist and some of the philosophic giants before him was the fact that he was dealing with the subject that had confounded them all alike. The least understood, most mystifying of all basic phenomena. The mystery of gravity.

Long before Newton it had been confounding, and afterward still. As another modern scientist Heinz Haber had written: "For years scientists have been studying gravity. They bracket it with life itself as the greatest unsolved mystery of the universe."

To go into that mystery Grover Schock had gone into his swimming pool and here he was, floundering with his new theories. In fact some of the mystery's most tantalizing aspects were the very things making him flounder (at least mentally) as he signaled other dim shapes and sucked air through his aqualung.

In the science of physics normal weight meant one G. The G was physics' own symbol for gravity. Immersed in water the body weighed less than one G, reaching the condition known as subgravity. There was even zero G—but never under water. For one thing the hydrostatic pressure restored some sense of weight. And the inner organs (heart, liver, lungs, kidneys, etc.) kept their own mean weight, reacting in a way that might have pleased Newton more than Archimedes.

But the whole thing was even more puzzling. Newton had defined gravity as the force exerted upon material bodies by the mass of the earth. Yet no inquiry on gravity had ever shown it to be related to anything but mass, or in other words itself. Not even physical or chemical conditions in the mass or even in the intervening medium ever changed it. And so in sheer isolation it had kept all its real secrets, the key to both its nature and source.

Which might have been all right once. Most of the Greeks were abstract scientists—even Archimedes disdained the practical as being unworthy the noble profession of philosophy. But in the advancing Space Age gravity was no longer a theoretical problem. The weight of a man's body in relation to the earth was his normal weight—but drive that weight up by great velocities and he blacked out into unconsciousness—or take his weight away and he fumbled all his movements and "lost" himself. At a force of ten G's even in a prone position he couldn't breathe. At any minus-force down to zero G he couldn't tell vertical from horizontal, down from up.

Yet velocities of almost seven miles a second were needed to pull him from earth's gravity into space. And in space when that initial velocity ended he was weightless because space was weightless, a human speck less than Newton's falling feather in the great outer void.

These (as Grover Schock knew only too well) were some of the many new problems—and instead of Newton's apparent weight what had to be defined was, for instance, the precise, functional, perhaps even fatal effects of such conditions on the human body itself.

Not that anything fatal was going on in the swimming pool. To the few onlookers it looked more like aquatic sport. It was an indoor pool, built on the campus of Alamogordo's School for the Visually Handicapped, whose board of trustees had willingly arranged for its part-time use. With Schock was his group of volunteers, all aeromedical chaps, and as some of them moved about under the surface in bathing trunks and skin-diving masks the only trouble was in telling who was who.

Except perhaps when Ed Dittmer got in, the biggest man physically in the group.

From Holloman they had trucked the ponderous 600-pound structure around which they were now working. First it had been assembled in a shallow part and then dragged to the deepest part. It was an odd-looking contraption, an iron framework with a ten-foot iron pole rising from its base, an iron chair that could be rotated around a four-foot horizontal pole, and a wide metal arc like the arc of a compass fastened in a half-circle across the vertical pole just behind the chair, scaled off in bold black lines and figures from zero degrees at the top to 90 degrees down each side of the half-circle.

The arc and the chair were the main features. At the back of the chair a long thin iron rod extended upward dissecting the scaled arc like a pointer—which is exactly what it was. It moved only with the chair, when the chair was moved.

With this contrivance task scientist Schock had worked out his own ingenious idea—to test himself and everyone else in the group for "perception of body positions, upright positions, and vertical and horizontal positions, following rotation in simulated subgravity conditions."

It was only one of many subgravity and zero gravity projects he was engaged in. In separate but related tasks he had been tackling such things as neuro-muscular coordination, vestibular response in jumping or jet-flown cats, oculo-agravic illusions in supersonic flight; weighty matters in the overall problem of weightlessness. As in the swimming pool, he sometimes had to devise his own tools. For instance a set of vertical-horizontal micro-ammeters for observing G changes during supersonic flight. Academically he was well founded in such subjects as zoology, electronics, the biological sciences. The results of many such projects were still occupying him now, interlocking with what he was doing in the swimming pool.

Now, while he waited, one man climbed into the ungainly looking chair, while two others assisted. They strapped the sitter in. Other figures hovered nearby. In their oxygen gear and face masks, some with swim-fins like immense webfeet, their movements stirred up rippling currents which distorted all their figures. Strong light beating down from outside made a dim transparent underwater cavern in which all of them, air bubbles rising from their heads, might have been taken for so many frogmen.

Though for that matter, weren't they subgravity frogmen?

Slowly, very slowly, the two standing by the chair began tilting the figure in the chair. They tilted him all the way around, down, and then up. Then again, and still again. The bubbles partially obscured him. Under the mask his face was further hidden by a blindfold. Blindfolding was a special part of the tests. So was the slow-as-molasses tilting. He was being completely disoriented visually, and losing all sense of real motion.

At a signal from the task scientist, the two assistants stopped the chair. The iron pointer, which had slid slowly around with the chair, now showed on the scaled arc a 42-degree tilt left of true vertical. Carefully, with arms outstretched, the chair subject did his own signaling, cupping or wiggling his hands, slanting his fingers. The two assistants tilted him as directed. With a final signal, meant to indicate that he now believed he was sitting exactly vertical, all motion was again stopped.

The iron needle pointed to 15 degrees left of vertical.

The experiment was tried again. Starting, as before, from the zero of the arc. This time the rotating was halted at 23 degrees left. The error was 4.5 degrees right.

On the third try the halt was at 31 degrees right, the error three degrees right. On the fourth try, from 36 degrees left, the error was gone, the iron needle pointing straight up! (One of the frogmen tried a small dance of excitement; it was webfooted, grotesque, and full of swirling ripples.) On the fifth and sixth attempts the error was back again, once by four degrees, once by seven.

At the end of the sixth try the man in the chair was unstrapped and the whole group began floundering toward the side of the pool, then scrambled out, whipping off tanks and face masks, some in sheer high spirits shouting like schoolboys, others scurrying for their cigarette packs scattered nearby. Schock paused to talk with tall Ed Dittmer who, as dry as the proverbial bone though in swim togs like the rest, had been stationed at the poolside all along, penciling exact notes for all the tests carried out that day.

"What did you get?"

"Completely across-the-board again. From zero to fourteen degrees in one subject—that was Bob Knox. Errors on Willis ranged from one to four-five. Alton Yates from four to fifteen."

Dittmer went on tabulating. Schock did a little jig of his own, shook a cascade of drops from his blond head, and eyed Dittmer in a way which showed obviously how much he liked the other. There had been a deep bond between the two men ever since the Manhigh III balloon accident and Dittmer's quick action.

In fact Dittmer had been his mainstay all through the underwater project. As he was a mainstay at the Laboratory itself—once a World

War II medic, a certified aeromedical tchnician now, closely associated with the Manhigh project, a C-47 tracker during all its actual flights, instructor for land, sea, and air teams in balloon capsule recovery techniques—and beyond all that, simply a tower of quiet confidence and strength.

"Any element of learning show up yet?"

"I'd say hardly."

"Well, let's try some more."

The dancing frogmen soon finished their break and were ready, still in a jolly mood, glad to be doing something for science but perhaps gladder to be doing it in such a pleasant way. Then they were all in the pool again.

In a way, what they were doing was as simple as sitting in a bathtub, dropping balls from a tower, pawing over a frozen chicken. The only thing in addition to simplicity being the intelligence behind the acts—which was everything.

And gradually, through these acts of his subgravity frogmen, Grover Schock had been getting at some of the facts he was trying to find.

It was interesting to note the wide variation in individual error. One of the original theories had been that in weightlessness any motion could lead to spatial disorientation. Most of the tests confirmed this. In the partial weightlessness of complete immersion many of the postural cues were reduced. This was dramatically shown in that all subjects could be tilted as much as 22 degrees off-vertical before becoming aware of any tilt at all. The chair-rotating mildly stimulated the semicircular canal system as well as the utricular mechanism, showed the labyrinth still functioning as in a normal gravity field—but this stimulation and the loss of vision made perception of the upright position almost entirely a function of the proprioceptive systems. There were mechano-receptors in the body for touch, motion, posture—the so-called kinesthetic sensations—but in weightlessness they lost their coordination.

Thus a man out in space could not function too effectively if he wasn't aided in some way. The muscle sense was gone. Without visual proof it was impossible to tell up from down. Under actual space flight conditions even the vestibular or balancing mechanism could not be relied on.

In short, man himself would need far more orientation in order to accustom himself to the thing called "the feel of space."

In the end there was much more to Grover Schock's findings. Detailed, minute, exact references to all possible effects; tabulations, charts, summaries, and conclusions; leading from Operation Swimming Pool to Operation Midnight Oil as he sat many a long evening in his small office or at home thinking over all of it.

Eventually the underwater investigations were added to the results of his other investigations; facts about jumping cats, jet parabolas, oculo-agravic targets, to name but a few again.

And then the real work began. Preparing all of it carefully, diligently, *demonstrably*, in science-paper form. But finally even this was done. Like almost all science papers bearing a long, long title (leaving brevity and wit for another day). "Some Observations of Orientation and Illusions When Exposed to Sub and Zero Gravity."

It was this paper, later delivered as his thesis at the University of Illinois, which earned him the distinction of being the first man in the United States to get his Ph.D. degree in a field as new as the Space Age itself—space physiology. (It also earned him a full professorship at the Air Force Academy.)

The *Journal of Aviation Medicine* reprinted the paper and then it was microfilmed and xerographed for the University's archives, a process certainly little connected with the things of Archimedes' or Newton's day.

Nevertheless as Grover Schock went about his new duties, reaching back toward those great minds as he taught fledgling scientists of the future, one could believe the other connections remained.

18

ZERO GRAVITY

Weirdest Feeling of All

BUT A DIFFERENT EXPERIENCE with the novel affair of weightlessness was in store for me—my own. It happened when the Project Mercury astronauts came to Holloman to go through their individual training in that gravity-defying state. After it was all over and the flying equipment was still there the word got around fast: would anyone at Holloman like to try it? The response was so immediate that the extra flights went on for another day, even after the famous group were gone again.

Not the least eager was our crew-cut colonel, who said: "Shall we try it?"

"Let's!" I said.

It was as simple as that.

To accommodate the Mercury candidates, two specially equipped and modified aircraft had been flown in from the Wright Air Development Division in Ohio, a C-131 transport and an F-104 jet interceptor, both scheduled to fly the fast parabolas or Keplerian trajectories to simulate this phenomenon of their future earth-orbiting journeys.

The objective at Holloman had been to subject each of the candidates to "at least thirty periods of maximum attainable weightlessness in a comprehensive test of mental and physical alertness." The C-131 flights had been accomplished at altitudes of 8,000 to 12,000 feet while the F-104 single-seater maneuvers had soared from 20,000 to 50,000 feet.

The more commodious C-131, appropriately titled "How High The Moon" in huge letters along its round fat fuselage, which also showed stenciled diagrams of diving spirals and upward parabolas thoughtfully marked with air speeds, pull-out times, multi-G figures and other exact flight profile data, was of course the experimental craft offered for Holloman's ex-officio flights.

Captain Wade, the slender coverall-clad aircraft director, gave us a short but vivid briefing even as we taxied out to a runway. Strapped in our parachute harnesses with separate chute packs under us we made a group of eight sitting among the dozen seats which had been left intact in the forward part of the plane.

"We'll stay upstairs long enough for all of you to get your turns," he said, "but for safety's sake it won't be advisable for more than two to be leaving your seats or floating at any one time."

He was addressing us from the rear of the craft which had been completely stripped of seats and other gear and then heavily padded everywhere, as effectively as any padded cell in a sanitarium. He went on to explain the nature of gravity research, the flight maneuvers through which it was now to be simulated, the emergency measures in case of aircraft failure.

"You all have your chutes and the escape hatch is right here." He indicated it. "If anything happens try to keep it an orderly process but don't stand too long on the order of your going." The grin that followed made it like any briefing from a mere "Fasten your seat belts please" to the physical demonstrating with Mae Wests on a MATS overseas flight.

Tenderly he brought each one of us a strong paper bag for another kind of emergency. "Also what you can do is remove your shoes now," he added, "because zero gravity doesn't necessarily mean zero momentum and you might find someone's foot in your face."

By this time the aircraft was roaring off the runway and in no time we were airborne. Shoes were tied to seat struts, the collective mood seemed as light as the flight. In fact a holiday mood. Most of those aboard were experienced pilots, and though none could boast of having been in orbit it was evident that all were eager to fly through the air with the greatest of ease.

Almost too soon it was happening. Although it left a blur in one's mind even for describing.

At an altitude that was announced as 12,000 feet the aircraft went into its first swift power dive.

As it plunged it gained speed, which was again announced . . . 190 . . . 230 . . . 265 . . . 290 . . . a roaring, rushing, pounding sensation but, more than that, an almost instant pinning into a single place and single pose that was like glue, like lead, like all the weight in the world suddenly exerting a viselike grip that took the breath away, pushed the seat up as if to force one through it, fixed arms and limbs in whatever way they had clamped themselves, made even finger-flexing an infinitely remote process only to be thought about, certainly not worth trying.

"You are now pulling two and a half G's."

At the bottom of the dive came the sudden pullout and 35-degree power climb. The weight became lighter—lighter yet—and still lighter—leaving all the tons of living entombment behind. The seat wanted to fall away. The buoyancy was all around, in the aircraft itself, which seemed feathery in its very framework and equipment.

And then we were weightless. Could any youth once on a Coney Island roller-coaster have even dreamed that its over-the-top effects would some day be among the most fascinating phenomena probed into by the new dreamers about space?

"All right for the first two—the rest hold yourselves down!" called the director.

Right there, for the plane load of Holloman astronauts, the fun began. Icarus and the Greeks would have loved it. Though in beatnik it was strictly like weird.

One following the other, the first two zero-G volunteers sent themselves floating half the length of the aircraft by a gentle push from their seats. They swam around like fish. Huge grins came to their faces—perhaps still mixed with a little astonishment. Eager calls from the sitters, suggestions, ideas for new improvisations; laughter and more faces showing bewilderment or disbelief.

With a slight jar and a new motor roar the pair of swimmers bumped rudely to the padded floor. The 70mm sequence camera clamped to a front seat alongside its operator stopped recording the goldfish-in-a-bowl scene.

The new power dive and entombment began. Roar and rush, iron in the blood, fearful and endless anxiety—and again the rising, delightful, feathery sense of leaving it all behind.

This time the two volunteers were more ambitious. Everyone was talking, ideas floated through the air like the floaters. Each of the pair (serious colonels both) achieved a somersault with a motion as easy as the upending of an actual feather—and grinned like children. One straightened out full length and walked like a fly along the ceiling. Delighted cries again from everywhere.

"Who's next—let's get on with this show!"

With a thump the show was over and then the pattern once more began—the dive and G pattern. The various time intervals for each part of the flight profile had been gone into—six to eight seconds for the 10-degree power dive, about 12 seconds for the power pullout, 15 seconds of pure weightlessness, generally two to three minutes between each full maneuver.

It was to be a 90-minute flight. And still the weightless periods were something fantastic. A chair occupant who happened to be retieing one of his shoes took his hand away and the shoe remained where it was, suspended gently alongside the seat with no visible support whatever. This caused others to pull objects from their pockets and try the same thing with notebooks, pencils, wallets—but no matter what its true weight the result was the same.

A flight surgeon bent on more serious experiment swam at full length through the air and tried to drink from the paper cup he was carrying. For a while the solid bubbles merely floated over the cup, but when the weightlessness suddenly ended the bubbles became water again and splattered all over his face.

For my own part of the proceedings I forgot at one point to anchor myself in the seat and likewise to hang on to the loosely stowed parachute pack, which began drifting away like something going out on the tide until free drift allowed me to follow and sheepishly snare it again.

Another flight surgeon squeezed food from a tube while floating and then had to chew industriously and swallow with a gulp. Others went through various additional antics—always at the rear of the aircraft which, as the director had also explained, was actually intended as a practical laboratory for studying both physical and psychological effects produced by this strangest of all space conditions.

One of the psychological effects, a profoundly curious one as it seemed, became more and more apparent in the increasing gaiety and good humor of everyone connected with the enterprise. As if this lightening of the human substance (the too too solid flesh) lightened the essence as well, inducing a mood of sheer playfulness. Or as one might have said with another questionable pun, producing levity through levitation.

However, there was also the slightly gray side—at least for this writer if not for the regular pilots who by now were experimenting even in their seats. For the accumulation of G forces built up some physical repugnance as well—being slammed down again and again under the iron viselike grip, feeling the breath crushed back in the lung cavities, the viscera moving, the growing queasy sense that was the basis of all motion sickness. Actually it was the change of G's and no G's. Foulest of repetitions. Ninety minutes. Approximately twenty trajectories, for a total of about five minutes of weightlessness in all, twenty G slams, body weight nearly 400 pounds, 400 times 20 . . .

The motor roared and time itself spun by and the skies went around and around, blue in their purity, enchanting in their gauzelike limitless space.

Then we were buzzing down and sailing quietly homeward again.

There was one slight coda to the tale. On the ground as I stood groggily wondering whether I wanted to be a space man or not I politely waited for my seatmate, Holloman's deputy commander Colonel (later Brigadier General) Allman Culbertson, who was conversing calmly with the aircraft director.

But the subject of their conversation was structural fatigue and theoretical aerodynamics and what if too many power dives in that type aircraft might have torn a wing off!

19

ORBITAL TRAINING

USAF Chimp Academy

EVER SINCE the early training days of Minnie, Tiger, Elvis, and Chang and then the great and famous days of Chang--renamed-Ham and the illustrious Enos after they blasted through the void helping to make space safe for humanity—the aeromedical laboratory at Holloman had been accumulating still more fame.

In fact it had become the source of such stores of chimpanzee information, notes, data, technical reports, scientific papers, news stories, pictorial spreads, incoming correspondence, and correspondence answered, that the job of sorting some of it for coherent telling seemed as confusing as Cape Canaveral trips might have seemed to the chimps themselves.

Some of the attention created by the flights seemed just as fantastic, if more amusing. Letters continued to come in from everywhere, requests for pictures and more news, for up-to-the-minute reports on how the chimps were doing, for chimp signatures and footprints and "paw" prints, for public appearances, for baby chimps as pets, for surplus chimps to be given to zoos. All the world had been in on the events and they were happy about it. From the "Spaceport" city of Alamogordo the Chamber of Commerce thoughtfully presented a plaque inscribed: AWARD OF SPECIAL MERIT presented to HAM THE CHIMPANZEE for aggressive leadership and faithful service as THE FREE WORLD'S FIRST SPACE TRAVELER.

From the U.S. Naval Air Station at Pensacola, came a space license plate and a picture of squirrel monkey Baker, the surviving member of the tiny simian pair who had preceded their big chimp cousins into space in the nose cone of an Army Jupiter missile. Also a gravely courteous request from the Navy to "see that Ham gets these for his mantelpiece."

From a real estate development in Texas the enthusiastic promoters sent a communication to "Mr. Ham Chimp" naming him as "the winner of one of these Vacationland building sites."

A food manufacturing agency wrote: "We are interested in doing a story of how Holloman Air Force Base has used monkey chow to feed the chimps."

One of the most amusing was still another agency letter requesting pictures "as our client's vaseline jelly is being applied to the chimps' elbows and knees for their rigorous trips into space—with a jar of our product shown in the picture." (Which suggested so ribald a reply as to what the client might do with his vaseline that it exceeded all the bounds of Air Force propriety to send it.)

All of which was on the lighter side of the two extraordinary flights and something even the space doctors had gotten used to. Nevertheless it was the serious results they were concerned with in busily studying all the details of both flights.

It was on January 31, 1961 that jolly Ham had blasted off from the Cape in front of a Redstone rocket for the 16-minute ride which took him 155 miles above the earth and 420 miles across the Atlantic at a peak speed of some 5,800 miles an hour. On November 29 of that same year it was saturnine Enos who soared up in front of an Atlas missile for a ride of three hours and twenty minutes to orbit the earth twice at velocities up to 17,500 miles an hour. All the world now knows the story of those flights and how the first "astrochimps" helped the first astronauts.

On Ham's journey the jamming of the thrust-rocket and early firing of the escape rocket caused added velocity so that the planned flight profile of 115 miles up and 290 miles out became a faster and higher flight sending him down-range well beyond the target area. On Enos' journey the eighteen global monitoring stations discovered trouble in the cooling and attitude-control systems thus bringing about the decision for early retro-rocket firing which eliminated the planned third orbit.

In both flights the pressurized space cabin, double-walled nickel-alloy capsule shell, Redstone beryllium nose shield, and Atlas plastic nose shield to ward off reentry heat, the flight panels, pressurized contour couches, life-support systems, cameras, communications equipment, command receivers, four-channel telemetry transmitters, tape recorders, radar tracking beacons, UHF recovery beacons and many other devices represented the most weird departure imaginable from the simple little chairs and masonite isolation chambers which had started their small passengers into this unearthly environment.

Nevertheless the psychomotor devices—three lights and two levers with simple lever pulls and avoidance tasks for Ham, three lights and three levers with much more complicated tasks for Enos—were the same familiar "instrument panels" they had always used; and like the trained and seasoned operators they were, each proved the value of his training and the magnificent work the space doctors themselves were doing at Holloman.

But the Holloman equipment likewise had been improving. Also the *Lebensraum*. Above all perhaps the professional approach—the arrival of a team of psychologists headed by one of the best of them, Major (later Lieutenant Colonel) Frederick H. Rohles, to establish a totally new section in the Laboratory, the comparative psychology branch, which had taken over all animal training.

The psychology branch had trained the Mercury chimps and then had gone on expanding. By the time the unfortunate Enos was dead of Shigella dysentery (an intestinal infection in no way related to his orbiting trip the previous year), Ham a retired veteran in the Washington, D.C., Zoo, and Fred Rohles a lieutenant colonel, the psychology branch with the Laboratory itself had spread from its few Vivarium buildings and some temporary quarters (at one time in a fire-house) to the more permanent space of a huge hangar-and-office building previously rife with an entirely different kind of activity: the training of Air Force blue-suit crews with Matador and Mace missiles.

And thus within the labyrinthine new building, as time went on, above all within the new training section of several immense bays with high ceilings, spotlessly clean, temperature-controlled, crowded with test chambers, restraint chairs, psychomotor devices, electronic program racks, telemetry devices, capsules fitted with sensors and recording instruments to register every kind of reaction—the chimp-in-space program had really come into its own.

Actually it had become a school for chimps.

To usher in the new students—diapered and wearing a nylon-mesh vest but no space suit—there were still the simple isolation tests or temperature and humidity tests while sitting in their metal restraint chairs.

(The restraint chairs were always needed if for no other reason than classroom attention plus the native strength of the animal itself. That strength was more than impressive. For instance a 50-pound chimp five years old could hold his own in a tug-of-war against a pair of handlers twice his size, and in pure mischief often did. Even more impressive was to watch an older male, 120-pound Paleface, as he nonchalantly lifted a 300-pound weight with one hand.)

For students a bit more advanced there were elementary psychomotor devices where they could be seen learning what it was all about and pulling their first sets of levers.

Others still farther along in their schooling might be carrying on the same tasks in full space suits and new and changed environments, for instance the simulated space environment of the plastic-enclosed contour couch.

Within the graduate training areas the near-diploma students performed their daily scholastics under still more sophisticated conditions, perhaps in a more highly evolved electronic-paneled test chamber or within one of the space capsules itself—doubly isolated in their individual couches, going through more complicated patterns involving multilevel reactions, tone signals, more complex time signals, also a variety of tasks in the process known as higher cognitive functioning.

The padded contour couches (again a far cry from primitive beginnings) included the same ones actually used in the Project Mercury flights. Moulded to fit the anthropometric measurements of the animal, made of plastic and designed for a supine position, each couch consisted of two halves which closed snugly about its nylon-suited occupant, with a transparent face plate and room for the psychomotor panel inside, also fittings for oxygen hoses through which 100% breathing oxygen as well as ventilation and pressurization could be applied to create a complete life-supporting miniature capsule system.

However, the psychomotor devices still remained the key to all behavioral progress—the business the psychologists were there for. Thus these too ranged a gamut from simplicity to sophistication. Some were still paneled with three lights, for instance blue, white, and red. These would be monitored by the animal in given reaction times, sometimes immediately, sometimes by delayed response, sometimes by multiple responses; all automatically programmed into the training pattern by means of the attached instrumentation.

For example, in one phase the animal might be required to pull his right-hand lever at least once every twenty seconds as the right-hand red light went on. This in turn would activate the center white light showing him that he had performed satisfactorily. At the same time the left-hand blue light might be flashing on a random schedule requiring lever response within five seconds. Also in more complicated tasks the response pattern might include a twenty-second wait before the lever pulling; quicker responses would reset a timer calling for a further delay of twenty seconds; after which the next light might cue the reward. (A squirt of water or the banana-flavored food pellet.)

Of the more sophisticated devices, some contained five lights colored blue, yellow, white, red, and green. Also for advanced training the lights could be replaced by symbols in order to present oddity displays (called IDD's or In-line Digital Displays)—again in sets of three, however, exposed on a dark ground-glass background, showing two identical symbols and one odd. The symbol could be a square, a circle, an X, a vertical dash, horizontal dash, a triangle, though these too could change since the basic objective called for recognition and thinking out by the animal. In symbol presentation the job of the animal was to select the odd sign much in the same way Stanford-Binet intelligence tests and visual-education appliances were used for children of kindergarten ages, though all performances were again related to given time responses.

But the psychologists were also experimenting with other mental applications; for instance, numbers. In what had turned out to be a fascinating affair even for them, the affair of learning and making use of chimpanzee perceptiveness, they were teaching the animals to count. This was done by means of a boxed display screen built into a thick-glassed test chamber in which the animal watched as any integer from one to four (in the Arabic) appeared on the screen. He banged his lever the same number of times. After a fixed total of correct responses (again programmed into the apparatus) he received his food pellet reward and the process started all over again—a process of positive identity and numerical recognition as proved by the high order of correct pulls.

Also the psychomotor devices had been developed into new types of panels, for instance, tracking devices. These were very much like earlier psychology-inspired devices used in complex coordination tests for selecting pilots. On one type the animal had to follow a moving target to receive his reward or avoid shock. (The same slight electric foot shock, which no self-respecting psychologist would ever have called an electric hotfoot!) On another such device, consisting of a ten-inch-square aluminum panel scored vertically and horizontally with a row of electronically activated movable lights, the subject had to match a red light in the horizontal row by moving a lever from side to side and a red light in the vertical row by moving a second lever forward or backward. When both red lights were brought side by side the pressing of a third lever presented a new set of lights and the animal was rewarded after every fifteenth correct alignment.

But perhaps the most unique training device, one in the realm of "higher cognitive functioning" indeed, was the Tic Tac Toe display. Actually it was a double apparatus, a matched pair of one-foot-square panels fitted at chimp eye height into the frameworks of two adjoining glass chambers so that both panels were perfectly visible to both animals. Each panel consisted of nine identical four-inch squares bordered all around the outer edges by blue button-size lights. The nine squares of one panel could be illuminated one at a time in solid red light and those of the other panel in solid green light from the electronic program rack whenever the Tic Tac Toe player decided to touch any particular square. The blue border lights were also connected with the rack and timed to go on alternately for each animal's panel as a signal that while the border was lighted he could touch any one square and play.

For that's what it was—the same competitive game played by children from times immemorial. As in all Tic Tac Toe games the object was for each animal to light his own squares in one direct line of three without being blocked by the other animal lighting his squares. Both panels lighted up simultaneously to match every touched square on either panel so that each player could see instantly what red was doing against green and vice versa.

Moreover it worked. Many times in their other forms of play the chimps' lively sense of rivalry had been noted by the even more lively minded psychologists. So—ergo!—the idea had been born. Then the apparatus itself had been developed. Later, with two of the older chimps (too old for capsule programs but old in intelligence too) the patient process of teaching had been carried out, this time using the positive reward principle only. But even the reward principle had become somewhat secondary, for rivals they had certainly become as they intently eyed their squares, knuckled this or that one with a touch, leered at each other and finished each game in nonchalant triumph (with food pellet in hand) or sulking defeat.

This was not only novel, it was so interesting to watch that even a high-minded psychologist could all too easily lose sight of the main objective, which again was to elaborate on the higher coordinates of chimpanzee learning in order to measure this gifted animal's true potentials as man's first assistant in the many spaces biology tasks reaching out toward the conquest of space.

These procedures had not only applied to psychology, however; in the new branch at Holloman they had also accounted for a good many of the actual equipment refinements. For instance, besides the psychomotor improvements and test chamber ideas, feeding and water devices had been developed that would function in actual space flight, namely during weightlessness.

This need had come about because conventional laboratory feeders in which food pellets dropped from a hopper into a chute were obviously impractical. Thus a solenoid-operated tube had been devised. When the solenoid was acted on, a food pellet was pushed from the tube and held by small plastic fingers until removed by the animal. The same sort of device for dispensing water in space flight had been developed with a cylinder kept under pressure against the solenoid valve and delivering a fixed amount (cued by a green light over the valve) when the animal bit on a drinking-tube switch that operated the valve.

The equipment was often of commercial make but the ideas and designs were mostly those of the branch itself, frequently of Marvin E. Grunzke. For instance it was Grunzke who had developed the feeding devices. As it was others who helped think up new psychomotor devices, test refinements, programming methods. In fact the small but talented crew who had arrived at Holloman to establish the branch— Rohles, Grunzke, Technical Sergeant Gordon Wilson, Airmen Robert Bush, Loren Bartrand, Marion Rathbun, civilian Richard Belleville, later civilian Donald Farrer, and Major Herbert Reynolds—consisted of four Ph.D. members, one with a master's degree and four with bachelor's degrees, a total high-caliber group that showed the way the Air Force itself was operating.

So they had all been gifted. Yet if one of them had to be named as the man who had flared with the highest enthusiasm, probed with the deepest insight, contributed the most techniques and helped the Laboratory gain its largest growth in facilities and importance as *the* chimpanzee research site of the free world, surely it was Fred Rohles.

20

THE ASTROCHIMPS

Next Step the Moon

THE ROHLES OFFICE, which had changed location several times over the years, finally slipping into the same long hallway as the von Beckh and Eli Beeding and other central offices, possessed one large framed cartoon which had followed its owner through all such organizational wanderings: a pen-and-ink sketch of two oversized mice, one lying on the floor of an enclosure propped on his elbows, regarding the other who leaned nonchalantly against the wall beside a long bar-lever. The caption of which read (with one addressing the other): "Boy have I got this guy conditioned! Every time I press the bar down he drops in a piece of food."

Once while I sat in his office admiring the cartoon as well as the man he told me some of the details of how he had come to Holloman.

"The days of space medicine in regard to animal study through psychology were very early days then. That was even before the Navy's Able-Baker monkey flights in 1959 and then the Sam and Miss Sam flights of our own monkeys from the School of Aviation Medicine. Also monkeys aren't chimps; their tasks were far less sophisticated and their performances in flight didn't stand up to those of Ham and Enos. At any rate, like all beginnings, those days had their own ups and downs— at one time there was a question of whether the new comparative psychology branch would even be continued. Luckily General Don Flickinger, our bioastronautics chief in Washington at the time, was more than interested. Another was Doctor James Henry who first launched the V-2 and Areobee monkeys."

I wanted to know more about the mouse training.

"But that was a real problem!" He threw up his hands. "Extremely difficult. With chimps we have something one can work with. But to teach a mouse to press levers and switches—!" He rummaged on his shelves and drew out a reprint of one of his scientific papers published in *Aerospace Medicine.*

"For this study we used a male C-57 BL mouse twenty-three weeks old. That's the black-haired Jackson strain you know, much hardier than the usual type, more useful too because at high noise levels they're not subject to audiogenic seizures—and because under radiation their hair turns white. A standard operant conditioning chamber with the lever removed was our test bed, and food deprivation started the subject off at eighty percent of its normal body weight. At this point magazine training was begun—within four weeks with thirty-minute daily training sessions the behavior was consistent and reliable on an FR-100 reinforcement schedule, in other words a fixed ratio of one hundred lever presses for one pellet of food."

The gleam of science was in the doctoral eye but still I wasn't getting what I wanted to know.

"How do you get the animal to do anything in the first place?"

It was a pleasure to find this gave him no problem.

"That's easy. The first key to conditional training is food deprivation. You start off by making the animal hungry and putting him in a box. The box has a food pellet slot but no lever to pull or press; the food is dropped in at intervals and by purely random movements the animal learns where it is. That's known as magazine training. Of course he also has to have the physical and neurological equipment to cope with the problem or else no response or test objective is possible. After that phase, the operator introduces a novel stimulus into the situation by attaching a lever inside the food pellet slot. Again the random movements of the animal take over; he finds the lever, presses it and is rewarded with food immediately. We call this continuous reinforcement, or one lever press for one pellet of food. Next we increase the number of lever presses he has to make for each pellet; like the piece-work principle of a given production schedule for a pre-fixed rate of payment. After this is accomplished the rest is only a further refinement of the basic principle, the deprivation-and-reward system which is really the motivating principle behind most of mankind's work—or isn't it?"

The gleam in the doctoral eye was back again in a milder but subtler form like that which had inspired all the philosophies of the ages together with their metaphysical contradictions and it was obvious in a flash how perceptive reasoning about Holloman's chimpanzees had made the training programs a success.

It was the mouse training which had led Fred Rohles to chimpanzee research, and until October 1963 when he left Holloman to accept a research professorship at Kansas State University, his abiding interest during those Holloman years was chimpanzees.

Another of the unusual Rohles enterprises at Holloman was that of establishing a college annex at the chimpanzee workshop, connected with the University of New Mexico at Albuquerque 200 miles away.

This was made possible because both he and Major Herbert H. Reynolds, the man who became the next chief of the comparative psychology branch, were members of the University's graduate faculty with professorial rank. Another who became a member of the "Holloman faculty" was Doctor Donald N. Farrer, who from then on divided his time between such subjects as "Chimpanzee Performance on a Continuous Avoidance Task During Acceleration at Sustained Low Levels" and the refined art of teaching a small class of students how to conduct such elements of chimpanzee research.

For that was the idea of the campus-away-from-a-campus—laboratory and classroom instruction in off-duty hours to Holloman officers, airmen, and civilians with biology or psychology majors and bachelor degrees in order to earn their master's degree in the field of psychology.

Moreover the little college flourished—and is still flourishing.

Also flourishing were the colony of chimpanzees and Holloman's Aeromedical Research Laboratory (which, like the Air Force Systems Command itself, had continued to expand and now formed a part of the Aerospace Medical Division of AFSC with headquarters at Brooks Air Force Base, Texas). For instance there was a chimpanzee named George who could now count up to nine. (Proved by the way he banged levers at his random-display apparatus.) Another named Lassie picked expertly from symbols such as crosses, squares, triangles, and colors. Just as talented a female, Shirley, reclined in a simulated space capsule operating her instrument panel by following visual and audio signals (light flashes and tone sounds). Still another tracked a moving target across a "radar scope" (oscilloscope screen) so efficiently that some of his handlers felt he could fly a beam in a spacecraft to direct its postorbit reentry.

And thus the aeromedical idea, which had paid off so handsomely in the Project Mercury orbits, was still paying off. Subjected to an increasing number of space-simulated conditions, using their psychomotor panels in humidified cubicles, in isolated capsules, on buffeting centrifuges and highly accelerated rocket sleds, in aircraft for both steady and turbulence-induced flight—all under the strictest and most humane rules for handling animals as established by the American Medical Association's National Society for Medical Research—*Pan troglodyte* was still demonstrating the fact that he was the most gifted and intelligent primate besides man himself in helping to answer the biomedical questions.

For instance in the National Aeronautics and Space Administration lunar program, chimpanzees had ridden the abrupt-deceleration apparatus known as the Daisy Track to determine what G loads a man could take and in what bodily positions to land him safely on the moon or elsewhere.

For the ICBM Titan program, with its use of exotic new fuels such as UDMH (unsymmetrical dimethylhydrazine), it was discovered that the fuel vapor itself impaired chimp behavior by causing nausea and performance decrements; this led to an extended program to study such effects on animals as a way of protecting ground launch crews as well as human astronauts.

In another planned program Holloman chimpanzees had been scheduled to share the ride with men on giant centrifuges (one man and one chimp to each ride) to study sight and hearing responses under increased gravity stresses; in particular to compare human and animal performance under identical conditions.

"For instance," Doctor Reynolds said, "in a study we asked Don Farrer to make with some of our chimpanzees on a smaller centrifuge over at White Sands Missile Range, where the Army helped us by operating the centrifuge, some unexpected results were found. It was noticeable that a force of four G's slowed each chimp down in his task reactions, but two G's didn't seem to affect any of them to any significant extent. But is this two-G resistance a natural immunity or is it just something the animal acquires? If so can man acquire it also? These are just a few of the new things we'd like to find out."

It occurred to me to ask him whether another noticeable factor in working with chimpanzees involved specially acquired abilities (even like G-force resistance) in special individuals—but with a twinkle more subtle than the Rohles twinkle he immediately pointed out that almost all young chimpanzees were good students, and went on to say:

"Just the same as in the Air Force, you know—it's the job that counts. Hence any job-rotations we have in our training programs here hardly succeed in ruffling a pair of bushy eyebrows."

He went on to elaborate how many chimps had been taught to count, match symbols, operate pushbuttons and levers, respond to light and tone signals, and other tasks besides. As a matter of fact our talk was taking place at a time when more than two hundred of these same animals had entered or passed through the colony—about a hundred of whom were still on hand, most of them less than five years of age and 50 pounds in weight, the most useful limits for aerospace research—and, as he again pointed out, a group like any well trained pilot group constituting a pool ready in many ways to act as Space Age trail blazers.

"Which is quite in keeping with our whole concept of Western civilization and its philosophy of the dignity of man," he added quietly but in a sudden classical departure that delighted me just as much as I had been delighted with the Rohles sallies. I waited for him to elaborate. And he did. He said: "On the phylogenetic scale it is man, essentially an animal himself of course, who stands higher than all other animals. Insofar as we know, however, the chimpanzee stands next highest, the most intelligent and 'human' of all other animals. He's a likable fellow, usually gregarious. He enjoys working with us as has been proved time and again. He learns to respond to the good treatment we give him. In fact through the progress of the Space Age he has become, as you might say, our working partner for such scientific advancements, therefore we not only make sure he has all the care and protection that a Glenn or Grissom or Carpenter received in opening up the space trails—he has this new role in history which has brought him closer to man and even made him a Space Age hero in keeping with the best of our Western traditions."

All this rolled off with the professorial ease and basic erudition I had noted in so many others identified at one time or another with this famous Laboratory.

But there was another thing too I was thinking about: that "care and protection" of the chimpanzee. For this as well was evident—and again the aeromedical premises, not to mention the staffs of psychologists, veterinarians, pathologists, technicians, animal handlers and other assistants had swelled. The full Laboratory complement now numbered over one hundred. The training areas had expanded, the Vivarium where the animals were housed and cared for had been completely modernized with scores of cages and runways both indoors and outdoors. The large hangar building itself had been made still larger, joined to a smaller building, and had been rebuilt inside to contain dozens of efficiently sealed-off laboratory rooms, clinical and treatment rooms, biochemistry and pathology sections, the most modern X-ray compartments, sterilization rooms and their equipment, a giant-size rotary-type cage washer, a special diet kitchen and special storerooms, surgical quarters, dressing quarters—and any number of comfortable office quarters.

With a Vivarium staff alone of more than 30 people, this part of the Laboratory and its facilities compared with any well-planned, well-staffed hospital offering the best that modern science could give for the care and well-being of its occupants.

Here the animals received routine examinations, medical treatment, complete physicals every quarter-annual period, including blood and urine analyses, EKG readings, blood chemistry studies, stool and throat cultures, full body-measurment inspections, X-ray examinations, metabolic studies.

One treatment room was reserved for fluid therapy applied by intravenous or subcutaneous channels for the care of sick animals. Special cages were on hand for animals in need of volatile anaesthetics. Another specially designed cabinet was there for oxygen therapy. And for general medical care this new Vivarium contained six isolation wards complete with portable cages and conveniently stored medical supplies such as the oral preparations and antibiotics which the veterinary doctors had found most useful in chimpanzee care.

Here also was Captain (now Major) Jerry Fineg, as wry-faced and expert as ever in his animal handling activities; chief of the Vivarium after having left Holloman for several years of duty elsewhere; back again at Holloman by self-confessed preference. It was Fineg who had been doctor-in-charge of the most famous chimps of the Space Age, Ham and Enos, when they journeyed to what was then Cape Canaveral, for their longer journeys away from the earth. And now it was Doctor Fineg who had something interesting to say about the psychology of handling his small patients.

"When you have a sick chimp on your hands it's almost like having a sick child," he said. "But we've found better answers for that problem —the illness, I mean. We simply treat them like children. For instance when drugs are available as pediatric preparations and we know children like them, it's a safe bet our chimps are going to like them in that form too. In other words we dispense with the pills and capsules wherever we can for the sweets and syrups."

Presently he took me on the most extended tour I had yet made of the new building. And once more I had to think of the few small buildings and cages in another part of Holloman from which had emerged this vast and scientific enterprise.

Among the new features was a 500-milliampere X-ray machine installed in a completely lead-sheathed room with a control console outside from which the equipment could be operated without any danger of radiation exposure to its operators. An adjoining darkroom and drying cabinet, also a viewing screen, provided for immediate readout of the many X-rays taken during periodic examinations of the animals.

The biochemistry laboratory, in addition to its use for refined studies in blood and urine analysis, had been equipped to handle more complicated procedures; for example radioactive isotopes that were useful in studying metabolic pathways of physiological reactions. For these advanced studies a Ph.D. biochemist had also become a member of the Vivarium's professional staff.

The pathology laboratory turned out to be a fully equipped post-mortem facility designed to provide support for all the work of the Laboratory, from autopsy through the processing and staining of tissues and microscopic study of the prepared slides.

The new clinical laboratory was equipped to handle most routine procedures involving hematology, serology, bacteriology, and parasitology. Likewise its more numerous technicians furnished clinical support for other aeromedical research activities, for example the almost daily Daisy track deceleration tests.

The well-lighted surgical suite, with special non-static flooring to avoid sparks during the use of combustible gases, appeared to be a fully appointed operating theatre and in fact, as I found, had been designed to handle most surgical problems.

And indeed one had to marvel at all of this. Hardly proper now seemed the rollicking days of old when a chimp might find himself being examined on top of any handy table; all was order and method and efficiency. And yet, as the handlers themselves pointed out (and as one could see), "chimpanzees were still chimpanzees." In the huge labyrinth of hallways and cage areas, in the clinical rooms and training rooms, there were still the antics. There was still the *huh-huh-huh-huh-huf-huf-huf-huf-huf-huf-huf* that got louder and louder like a banshee scream as the screamer let out in sheer high spirits. Still the tug-of-war groups, the water squirters, the mimics and imitators who seemed to be making fun of everybody including themselves. Perhaps even becoming more "human."

For there were also, now, more of the physiological wonders coming to light. Besides training *Pan troglodyte* to become a potential spaceman the space doctors were continuously finding out these other factors which, like another quaint form of serendipity, constituted the fascinating and humanly helpful by-products of space research. For instance the iron-binding protein in man and chimpanzee had been found to be a new physiological link. Diseases like arteriosclerosis, hardening of the arteries, hepatitis, even syphilis had been added to the growing list of mutually common infirmities. In fact the biological relationship was being explored so intelligently that similar factors were again found in the form of anti-serum, that part of the blood which contains its own disease-fighting elements or antibodies; guardedly the aeromedical doctors admitted (with that understandable caution which accompanies all new scientific discovery) that a request from a communicable disease center of the nation's Public Health Service had been answered by supplying anti-serum from all the chimps at Holloman, also their complete medical histories.

In the same guarded way it was being disclosed that another giant step in the man-chimpanzee linkage had been involving these same animals at Holloman; this time in the surgical field; by implanting chimpanzee kidneys in humans. The medical doctors even more than the "space doctors" (if one could make such fine distinctions) had been responsible for such discoveries. And by the very nature of the Holloman areomedical work, likewise because of the size and utter uniqueness of its chimp colony, the finest medically maintained colony of its kind in existence, it was not only inevitable that such discoveries should have been made, but that both civilian and military research teams throughout the rest of the medical world should begin beating a path to the Holloman aeromedical door.

And so Pan troglodyte had become even more inseparably linked with Homo sapiens. Which was causing Homo sapiens—again by the very nature of things—to extend him more and more consideration. For instance, if the famous space traveler Ham had left his comfortable Washington Zoo quarters for a Holloman visit some years later, he might have been a little envious despite the luxuries known in Washington.

For one thing, the way of life of a chimpanzee at Holloman had become so improved by factors like dietary control and clinical protection that the statistics (in the form of baseline studies) seemed to show physical improvement as well; most of the animals appeared to be both stronger and healthier than they could have been, conceivably, in their native habitat. This was even leading to the thought that possibly longevity as well could be involved; in other words, with such good care for a lifetime might they not again emulate their human brothers and simply live longer?

For another thing, there were the improved cage areas: their living quarters. Like any modern apartment building built for the comfort of its inmates these quarters were not only spacious but equipped with the creature comforts, for instance heat, light, running water. They were furnished with playthings as well as the kind of swinging perches that had been found a most popular item with their tenants. Also, each individual room opened upon an outside patio so that the entire community could socialize out-of-doors to their hearts' content—which they usually did in the sunny New Mexico weather.

But above all, the newest improvement of all took on shape and substance amid the dry and barren wastes of the Southwest as an oasis, a jungle, a truly representative natural habitat, with trees, vegetation, and the very look of the wilderness where its only denzens, the chimpanzees of Holloman, could really live in arboreal freedom. By 1965 the project had begun and by mid-1966 was well under way, with transplated oaks and elms already beginning to dot the enclosure, stretching their gnarled arms skyward to give a strange new look to some of the Holloman landscape.

And what matter if the development did bear the more-than-awkward title: Primate Source Consortium? It could as easily have been called Chimpanzee Eden without offering any more than was planned. A moat had been built to keep the area within reasonable boundaries, and a fence was to keep out unwanted intruders, either two-footed or four-footed. This had been the envisioned scene long before a spadeful of earth was broken or one piece of shrubbery carted in. For it was indeed a shrewd and far-sighted project (perhaps not only with science but with sentiment in it) thought out in detail by Jerry Fineg and other space doctors for their most promising animal space candidates. In fact would it not allow his still further development by further improving his lot and way of life? Could it not even lead to natural breeding habits? —a factor that had been found almost absent in the existence of early captive chimpanzees who seemed to need natural instruction and imitation for such activities.

So all this was in the minds of the doctors, as well as the subtle philosophical concepts with which they weighed the many meanings of freedom itself. And though the Primate Source Consortium remained a ponderous title for such an abode, nevertheless it seemed like another unique Air Force approach toward solving the pressing biomedical problems of the Space Age.

21

SPACE ARITHMETIC

The Desk Calculator With a Brain

IT WAS TRUE that Holloman's chimpanzees and their antics had always been the greatest source of fascination. But there were certain other Holloman activities, for instance the inertial guidance testing, the computer processing, the data reducing, which, even as the years passed, had held their own fascination by remaining the greatest mysteries. Nor did exotic reading like *Electronics For Everyone* furnish enough of the answers.

The Delphic spot for answers had been the data reduction center and in some instances the guidance test center itself.

The long, low, E-shaped building in the West Area which had been Holloman's first data processing site contained a cluster of tri-helix telemetry antennae on the roof (for real-time range signals) which was rather reminiscent of both King-One and the high-speed test track's Midway building. However, the first glimpses indoors would have belied one's ideas of any of the rest of its activities. Long, narrow corridors, endless small rooms, men working quietly at desks or discussing matters at blackboards, a calm reposeful atmosphere like that of any well-conducted office building. Where then were the electronic frenzies and the computers?

The first such clues were names on organization boards or office doors; names to conjure with in the hierarchy of science people. Doctor Ernst Steinhoff, chief scientist, once a top figure in Germany's Peenemunde operations. Doctor Gerhard Eber, chief research consultant and wind-tunnel master who had worked out all the intricacies of the Holloman test track. Doctor Harold Melkus, chief research engineer. Doctor Herbert Knothe, chief mathematician. Doctor Martin Jaenke, chief project analyst. Major (later Lt. Colonel) Herbert Barker, computation chief and author of books on such subjects. And a good many others— names like Penzig, Hoehndorf, Gschwind, Ehni, Manz, Jahns, Borges, Tantzen, Lotze, Woehl, Schneider—so many of them German names as well, some like Steinhoff from the famous Peenemunde lists, others from various places in Germany but scientists all; physicists, mathematicians, computer experts, experts in the higher branches of engineering.

And if the names were only clues the next evidence was the real thing, found within the broad E wings, where only a few offices were located—and for the rest vast open spaces lined with orderly rows and ranks and tablesful of paneled and cabinet-held equipment so complex looking, with such an assortment of dials, switches, meters, spinning tape reels, moving lights and counters, oscilloscope windows endlessly running their green-eyed blips, patch-wires, programming panels and other electronic devices everywhere in the immense room, that it could have been nothing but the data processing and computer reducing that was the Delphic scene itself.

Though here it was men running the machines instead of harried mortals looking for a *deus ex machina*. Mathematical certitude accomplished with electronic surety, as even a writer-visitor might know, even if he would have known nothing else except for the men themselves. (Such as Major Barker, chief Jahns, engineer Schneider, technician Zimmerman who nursed the machines—professionals who again were used to explaining their activities to non-professionals.)

They named things.

The data collecting equipment such as ground stations, converters, time code readers, programmers. The display equipment such as analog and digital plotters, oscilloscope recorders, frequency analyzers. The vibration equipment: wave analyzers and more wave analyzers. The accessory equipment like signal conditioners, tape testers, magnetic tape handlers.

They described things.

The three ground stations were in a sense connecting links with the Midway complex: numerous cabinets of panel equipment through which all raw tape data had to be fed to unscramble the original signals. At the Midway the many data bits from each sensing device in the sled-borne telemetry package were recovered on multiple-track tapes; at the data center's ground stations these were filtered out into separate channels again and demodulated to make other tapes and playbacks.

From there the tapes were fed into the converters. (Again large multiple racks of instruments, panels, wires, switches, banks of small oscilloscope screens, many more devices.) In the analog-to-digital converter each data track went through processes to change its continuous form to discrete forms measured against given time intervals, for instance, 24,000 intervals per second. The measurements were then fed into the computer to come out in terms of digital language, in other words as tabulated figures in numbered form.

In turn the digital-to-analog converters retranslated such digitized information, for instance large quantities of numbers too bulky to be used for practical analysis, into forms that came out of the analog computer as plotted or graphed results.

(The analog computers were measurers, the digital computers were counters. The analog worked with resistances, continuous signals in the form of electrical voltages. The digital—often called "the desk calculator with a brain"—worked with numbers, time-and-event samples, and numerically printed readouts.)

In both kinds of conversion the plotters and programming devices came into play for preparing and handling the computer output.

The tapes were also fed into the time signal code readers, large double cabinets with a row of voltmeters positioned over many more rows of programming knobs, so that certain time intervals could be prepared for display through the oscillograph recorders.

The oscillograph recorders with their rolls of photo-sensitive paper, some with stylus-like pens, some for high-frequency and some for low-frequency signals, produced the oscillograms that were useful in determining function-versus-time results, for example the microsecond changes in voltage or acceleration or pressure conditions picked up from the object that had been tested.

From other parts of the data tapes, the various kinds of wave analyzers or frequency analyzers produced still other displays to be analyzed, for instance vibrograms showing power-spectral-density plots of vibration conditions, also power-versus-time plots for changes in vibration intensities, or even combinations of such results.

There was also the signal conditioning equipment; double cabinets of panels showing many tiny oscilloscope screens, amplifiers, and attenuators. This equipment was used to recondition poorly recorded tapes, for instance, those on which imperfect telemetry signals might have produced mixtures of signals. By means of filters or amplification each track on the tape itself could be cleaned up to go through the rest of its processes.

Several magnetic tape handlers were being used to make playbacks or to record selected data on new tape.

Another item of accessory equipment was the tape testers, clever devices for evaluating the quality of various commercial tapes, also for testing second-hand tapes which could be economically useful for local playbacks. There was more equipment. Much more.

And there were the computers.

Behind the large open space of the data processing section (the size of a normal school auditorium), a second glass-enclosed section about the same size housed the two 1103A Univacs. (Until later in the Holloman picture when even they were gone.)

Like so many "electronic brains," they were monsters.

Solid rows of steel cabinets the length of the room held the interior instrumentation and its thousands of vacuum tubes all neatly positioned in their individual panels. Continuously refrigerated, the panels were cold to the touch, as were the outsides of the cabinets. In front of each computer was its station console, a panel-inset crowded with hundreds of indicators, switches, push-buttons used to find and analyze its own trouble spots, control knobs, for countless operations including an asynchronous input-output able to handle, with its loading platforms, as many as 512 separate word-auxiliary memory cores.

Imbedded in the panel at the top of each console, in raised gothic, was the name of the brain: UNIVAC SCIENTIFIC.

The very sight of such a complex (the Delphic shrine itself) called for still further details. It turned out that both computers had been specially modified to handle the large volumes of data produced by flight tests, sled tests, and aeromedical tests, the three major forms of data reduction at Holloman. One computer had been equipped with built-in floating point arithmetic. Computer input was accomplished by magnetic tape or punchcards; output by punchcards, punched tape for translation into plotted graphs, recorded tapes for use in other equipment, also by a high-speed printer which then produced paper listings.

The people who were describing these details seemed justifiably proud of their computer shrine.

"We also have a Pace analog computer in another building wing," said the tall German-born Jahns—with the faintest trace of accent but choosing his words with characteristic care. (He too had been one of the Peenemunde group with von Braun, had come right along with Operation Paper Clip to America.) "We must visit the Pace too—for instance, it has four identical consoles that can be operated separately on separate problems or by slaving two together for more complicated problems. But first I'd like to sum up what we are doing here and how our Univac operations work."

He cleared his throat and went on as carefully as a schoolmaster.

"It will be obvious that our job here is to compute the performance of missiles, inertial guidance systems, and all kinds of sled-borne test items for quick and accurate data. The data output is used to tell how the mechanical and electrical components of the test items work under abnormal conditions like high acceleration, high onset, extreme vibration, rapidly changing temperatures and other stresses. We analyze both optical and electronic information received through our telemetering systems. For instance we did this on our Minuteman tests, where the inertial guidance gyros and velocity meters were mounted on the sled so that both sled telemetry and autocollimators at fixed intervals along the track could provide data on their environmental stability and calibrate the acceleration devices which measured the test velocities. Also with our telemetry ground station tie-ins we handle both analog and digital information and this processing includes reception, linearization, digitizing, storage, display, and computer input. Almost all the telemetry information reaches us on magnetic tape, and in analog or continuous form. This has to be broken up in sample form and numerical readouts by our analog-to-digital converters. We then transcribe it on to digital tape and feed it into one of our two Univac computers. In fact we can convert the data back into analog form as well; we do this on a sixteen-channel converter after which it's ready for the plotting tables and visual display.

"So you see, therefore, in all these ways we furnish the analyses needed by the test people and design engineers to let them know how each component in the inertial guidance system or some other test item has been behaving."

So at least Walter Jahns had said. But in time there were other things to be said—and learned about computers as well. For in time even the famous Univacs had not been enough for the always growing Holloman workload; like old but faithful plow horses they had been put out to pasture and in their place existed a sleek, transistorized, modern unit that was soon being described by its new computation chief, Tantzen, in even more glowing terms than the quiet Jahns would have used.

"This is what we call a CDC 3600 computer," he said, sitting at its massive tri-sectioned console and fingering its controls as affectionately as any pianist running over the keys of a beloved Steinway. "Do you know what this thing can do? For one example, right now it's making ten thousand calculations while I blink one of my eyes." He blinked it. "Its printers are running off a thousand lines of tabular matter in the time it would take me to hand-print one line. The CDC, by the way, stands for Control Data Corporation. Actually it's only a part of a

Trinity Site—Where the first atomic bomb in history was exploded.

Target Practice—A B-50 bomber prepares to take off with an XQ-4 supersonic drone.

Opposite above:
Tracking A Missile—At King-One radar tracking station on White Sands Missile Range.

Opposite below:
Missile Launch—A Matador thunders up from Holloman.

Drone Mission—A C-130 Hercules drone launcher in the skies over
Holloman.

THE LONESOME BUBBLE—Inflating a target balloon for missile practice over the range.

PROJECT MANHIGH—Lieutenant Clifton McClure prepares for his 100,000-foot balloon ascent.

PROJECT MANHIGH—The sealed capsule with McClure inside ready for dawn lift-off.

Opposite above:
BALLOON RESEARCH—Chief meteorologist Duke Gildenberg plots a balloon flight from Holloman control room.

Opposite below:
BALLOON RESEARCH—This glistening polyethylene bag carries aloft delicate instruments to probe the earth's atmosphere.

OPERATION HIGH JUMP—Captain Joseph Kittinger takes off in an open balloon gondola to jump from 20 miles above the White Sands Missile Range.

Operation High Jump—Resembling a visitor from outer space Captain Kittinger peers through his pressure helmet before a long, lonely leap from the sky.

OPERATION HIGH JUMP—After a record-breaking leap: "I'm very glad to be back with you all, gentlemen."

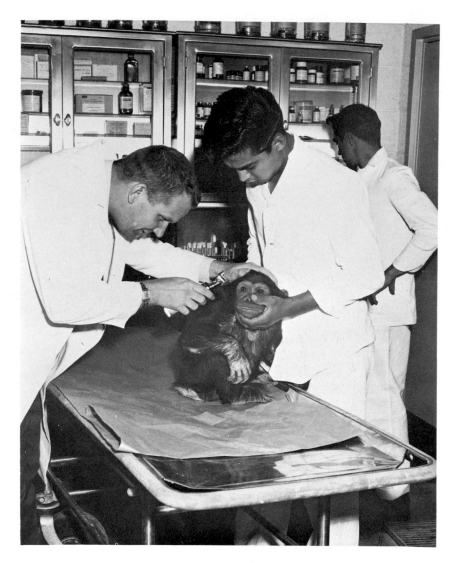

DAILY CHECKUP—Doctor James Cook uses an otoscope in examining one of his young charges.

Opposite above:
PLAY TIME—Aerospace doctor Jerry Fineg and technician Alfredo Martinez teach a new space candidate that not all research is work.

Opposite below:
SPACE ANIMAL—A young chimpanzee breakfasts daintily at Holloman's aeromedical laboratory where these animals have proved invaluable in space research.

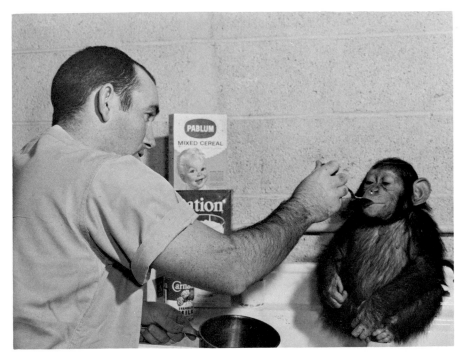

Opposite above:
SUPERSONIC BASEBALL—This 155-mm howitzer fired a shell that was caught in flight by a rocket sled.

Opposite below:
SUPERSONIC BASEBALL—This 10,000-pound sled caught a howitzer shell in supersonic flight.

SPACE AGE TRACK—These asbestos-clad technicians gingerly handle their fuel lines in readying a liquid-engine rocket sled for a supersonic track run.

SUPERSONIC BASEBALL—Cushioned with foam rubber and celotex this rocket sled was the "catcher's mitt" which caught an artillery shell "pitched" by a 155-mm howitzer.

Opposite above:
ROCKET SLED—On Holloman's captive missile test track this 114,000-pound-thrust triple-chambered sled blasts off at more than 1,000 miles per hour to test a missile guidance system.

Opposite below:
SLED DAMAGE—Built of quarter-inch armor-plate steel, this 3,000-mph test sled was torn open by impact with one small bird during a test run.

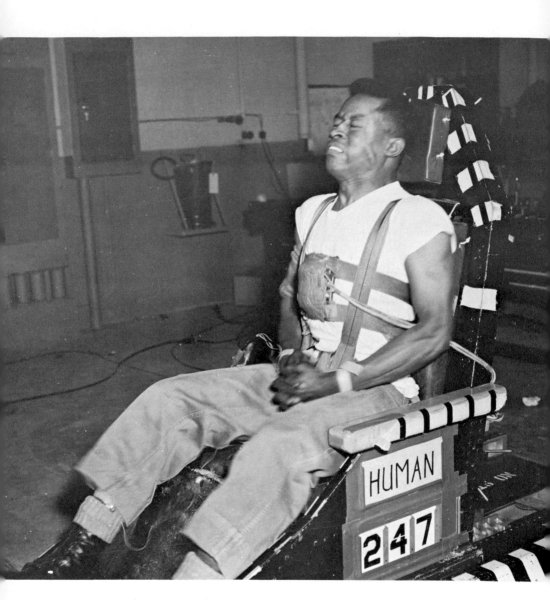

THE BOPPER—On a 20-foot sled-and-track decelerator, Lab technician Alton Yates experiences multiple-G forces in an abrupt stop.

FASTEST MAN ON EARTH—Colonel John Paul Stapp rides a rocket sled at 632 miles per hour.

DAISY TRACK—Colonel John Paul Stapp and Captain Eli Beeding prepare a volunteer for abrupt deceleration ride.

Opposite:
DAISY TRACK—Pressure suited, strapped in a model space capsule seat, a volunteer rider awaits a high-G impact ride for reentry studies.

DAISY TRACK—Eli Beeding receiving 83 G's at the instant of impact in an abrupt deceleration ride.

Opposite:
MULTIGRAVITY FLIGHT—Ready for takeoff in an F-94-C flight to study the effects of multi-G blackout.

SUBGRAVITY EXPERIMENT—Holloman airmen share in research task to study gravity theories as old as Archimedes.

Opposite above:
ZERO GRAVITY—What happens in a flight-simulated experiment with weightlessness.

Opposite below:
"HIGHER COGNITIVE FUNCTIONING"— A chimpanzee learns the game of tic-tac-toe to compete with a brother chimp in this by-product of space research tasks.

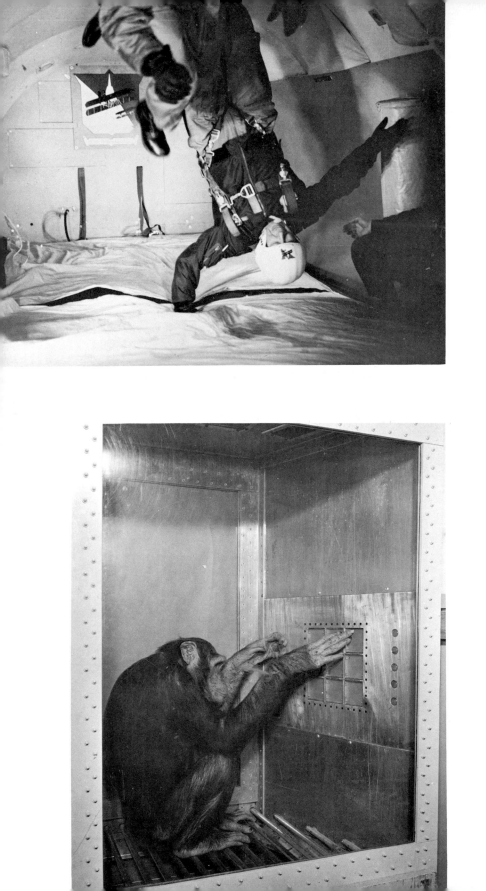

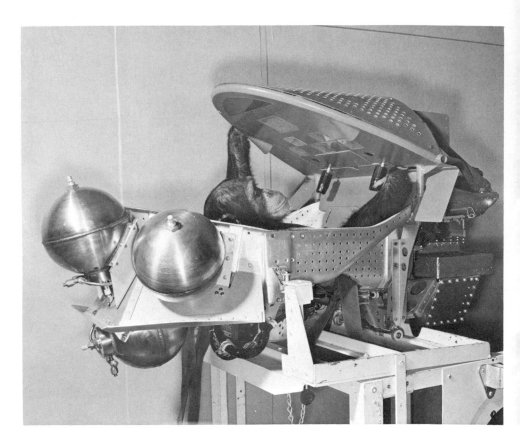

ORBITAL RESEARCH—Studying psychophysiological responses to discover how man himself might respond in space.

SPACE CHIMPS—Ham (left) and Enos casually resume their space training after Project Mercury flights that blazed the trail for human astronauts.

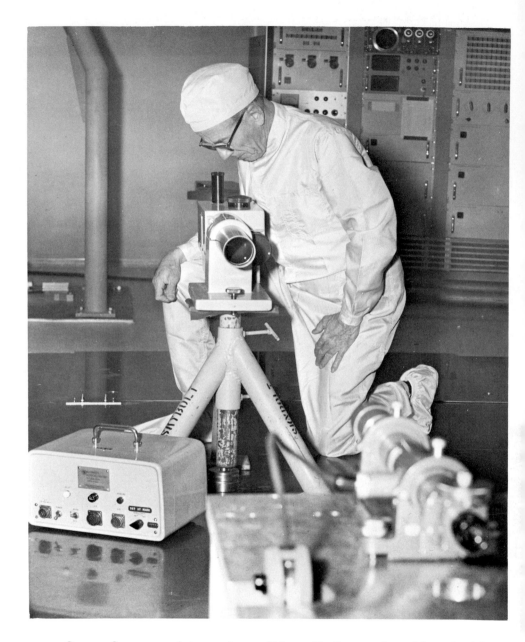

SPACE STEERING—Astro-engineer Edgar Godley works with celestial-inertial guidance test equipment designed to help spacecraft steer more accurately through the stars.

STRATOSPHERE CHAMBER—The giant test chamber behind this console can simulate pressure, humidity, temperature, solar radiation, and vibration conditions from zero altitude anywhere up to 225,000 feet, to test such effects on men and equipment.

SPACE ARITHMETIC—This CDC 3600 digital computer is so fast it can perform 10,000 additions in the time it takes to blink an eye.

SATELLITE TRACKER—A Holloman physicist, Walter Woehl, is seen making adjustments on the 25-barrel image-orthicon Facet-Eye camera he developed, the first of its kind in the world.

RATSCAT—The Radar Target Scatter Site on the White Sands Missile Range collects radar reflectivity measurements on missiles and spacecraft.

ALAMOGORDO, NEW MEXICO

READY FOR A MISSION—High over the White Sands Missile Range this Holloman crew will seek to evade a "hit" by a deadly missile in simulated aerial warfare—taking along the author of this book (at right) to do the story.

more complete computer system we've installed; for instance there's a CDC 160-A we use by linking it with the main unit, also a CDC 8090 we've placed over in our guidance and control directorate for faster handling of all the data accumulated in inertial guidance testing."

He went on speaking with a kind of dry matter-of-fact intensity that was even more impressive, and, as it seemed, characteristically German, like himself. (He had been at Holloman since 1953, another of the scientists reaching the States through Operation Paper Clip—born in Oldenburg, schooled at Hannover, later a member of the same Peenemunde rocket electronics group once headed by Ernst Steinhoff.)

"We installed this CDC 3600 system for about three million dollars —though I don't mean *I* did it," he corrected himself quickly. "It's completely transistorized. Our Univacs were the vacuum-tube type. This makes a difference both in speed and space. For instance the CDC 3600 takes up only half as much room. It also does the work both Univacs did, and does it six times faster. Because of its new kind of logic circuitry it does lots of things simultaneously, like printing, plotting, card reading—and carries on its computing job at the same time. For instance our old computers took on one problem at a time. Now it's as if our CDC 3600 says to us: 'I can take all your problems at once and work each one as I come to it.' You see?"

He grinned, and immediately went on.

"The two special abilities of computers," he said, "are problem solving and speed of operation. The larger a computer's internal memory capacity is, the larger the problem it can solve. The more advanced in its design it is, the faster it can operate. Now our Univacs had only 20,000 words of memory whereas this computer has 32,000 words. For each word there are forty-eight bits of magnetic core storage—that is to say, internal memory capacity. So we now have over a million and a half bits for problem solving where we had less than a million before. But also, for another half million dollars we hope to extend our present capacity to more than three million bits—which compares well with the present state of the art and should handle our computation workload very well here at Holloman."

While I was still digesting that he again went on, leaning back as he remarked more meditatively: "We also have more data links and ease of communication. For instance by placing our smaller CDC 8090 computer at the guidance directorate with its own data link—a telephone line carrying computer signals instead of human talk—we've been able to shoot data back and forth that we used to carry by hand. In fact with the CDC 3600 we can accept data from anywhere on the White Sands Missile Range for direct processing. We can also operate in real-time for a missile in flight being followed with external tracking."

So at least some parts of the electronic mystery had been revealed. There was even some further unraveling of the long-puzzled-over telemetry mystery—at another moment and during another exploratory visit to the Delphic scene where all such matters fomented. By as unique an analogy as it was simple, the offering was made by engineer Schneider.

"You can think of Indian smoke signals as one of the first forms of telemetry," he said—and there was a gleam in his eye which could have been either truth or sheer amusement. "Like this . . . one Indian on a hill wanted to tell something to another Indian on a hill. So he used smoke puffs. By interrupting the puffs he modulated his signals. Of course both Indians knew the code. So they could signal each other. They needed an information carrier—that was the smoke. In modern telemetry it's a radio wave. The modulating is done by breaking up the monotony of the signal—that's known as amplitude or frequency modulation. In place of the Indian receiving the signals, there is the equipment to read and translate the codes back into reality. And telemetry is as fast as the smoke signal—which of course could be seen at the speed of light, which is also the speed of a radio wave."

He was still smiling mysteriously as I made my exit.

And then there was more to be learned about Josef "Peps" Schneider himself, also Walter Jahns, two closely working members of the computer shop who had earned equal fame by creating another important electronic device.

(Not that they were really alike—the fatherly slow-speaking Jahns, born in Brunswick, V-2 rocket developer; and fun-loving Munich-born Schneider, staff communication officer during the war, accomplished violinist, usually more lively than meditative. Both of them diploma engineers with master's degrees.)

Between them they had invented and built the electronic device, an Event Time Reader.

"We call it the ETR for short," remarked Major Barker as we sat in his small office alone, "and it came about because we had to develop a faster more efficient readout of telemetered data during advanced testing of the Minuteman and Titan inertial guidance systems."

Inertial guidance systems were another part of the mystery I had wanted to track—but conceivably the major was not aware of that.

"What we really needed," he went on, "was a space-time readout unit. In other words a more reliable velocity measuring system. A missile's inertial guidance system contains its own computer. When we install it for test on a high-speed sled and run it at high Mach numbers to simulate a real flight, it puts out pulse signals indicating where it thinks it is in relation to a given starting point. These pulses are telemetered from the sled to our FM/FM ground station and recorded on magnetic tape in intervals of microseconds—millionths of a second. Unless the time readouts are completely accurate our engineers never know whether the inertial guidance computer really does know where it is in space-time continuity; consequently they can't determine the accuracy of the system which is needed to control a missile in flight."

Quietly, in measured words, sometimes with scribbled diagrams, the tall and rather professorial-looking major who was also an engineer as well as a computer specialist went into further details.

"We discussed this problem with Walter Jahns who presently conceived the idea for the new unit—and with Peps Schneider who designed and built it."

The diagrams and his words indicated what had been built: a double cabinet full of its own complicated assortment of circuits, wires, switches, amplifier and generator, control panels and a score of control knobs, all labeled by its abstract title, which was evidently anything but abstract to the speaker as he described how the unit did its pulse-counting work of reading out telemetry tapes fed into it from endless guidance system tests.

"At first it digitized down to the nearest ten microseconds for each time of occurrence after first motion. Then with further improvements by Schneider plus the slowing down of the tapes themselves, it produced time-pulse readouts to the nearest 1.25 microseconds. Now it's even more improved with a lot of new circuitry able to handle PCM telemetry as well as every kind of data reduction project involving the digitizing of events in time."

His pleasant eyes studied me mildly and I sat there stunned—right back at the point where I had known nothing about nothing and knew it was nothing.

My plight must have made itself obvious.

"Suppose we try to say it in another way." He smiled, frowned, thought so intently that it put lines in his forehead. "The Event Time Reader reads the time difference between two or more events. The basic principle is to turn one of the two counters on while the other is turned off by the same event pulse. The system gets a synchronized switching with the count clock and no counts are lost. A first motion pulse allows the reduction of the readings to the absolute time scale. Noise pulse suppressions prevent any fouling of the reading cycle. Editing provides the selection of any number of events from one up to one less than a million."

This time I had stopped thinking at the word "lost"—clutching at it with every mental concept that equated my own position with that of "first motion."

He shrugged sympathetically but resignedly.

"I suppose it's as much of a problem as testing the inertial guidance systems themselves. But let's try once more. For instance if you have an event happening, say a velocity increment from an accelerometer, it happens at a point of exact time in relation to a system time base— say a clock. So if you feed the record of the event into the ETR, all you need is to feed in a time reference with it. The ETR then puts a time tag on that event and we know its space-time reality, in fact down to one microsecond of accuracy. Really it's only a timing system —but advanced so far you could never really use the ordinary word *clock*."

I had begun dimly to see the light again and hastily decided that was my own stopping point.

But I no longer felt up to the final question still loitering within my numbed interstices . . . just exactly what was an inertial guidance system?

22

SPACE STEERING

The Inertial Guidance Miracle

"WITHOUT A GUIDANCE SYSTEM a missile is nothing but an overgrown pyrotechnic toy," said Lieutenant Colonel Carl Roemer. "And an impotent toy at that."

With this vivid analogy I had been introduced into the guidance mystery—keeping hot on its trail as it led back to Holloman's North Area once more, not too far from the chimp colony's new quarters, in another vast hangar-and-office building full of totally different activities.

There its tracks had not only led to more books, talks, and technical reports but had crossed still profounder mysteries, Newtonian Laws of Motion, gravitation, gyroscopic principles, celestial navigation—things which constituted the heart of the matter not only for missiles but every target-aimed vehicle of the Space Age.

Whether the target was a point in the Urals or a crater on the moon or an interstellar voyage in deep space it seemed that the miracle steering of an inertial guidance system, or in its larger aspects a celestial navigation system, had to be the vehicle's method of finding its way there.

(No explanation of such a phenomenon could possibly remain too simple. But once on its track I had determined to simplify it for myself.)

The word *inertial* had become another key to unlock some of its profounder meanings. Concerning guidance systems it related to the Newtonian First Law of Motion which defined inertia as that property of a body which tends within itself to resist changes in motion.

Thus the inertial guidance system had gotten its name from the fact that it measured motion according to Newton's inertial laws—needing neither radar, radio, nor any other external unit to control, direct, adjust, change, or otherwise help it find its destination.

In fact outside conditions such as wind, weather, radiowaves, magnetic currents had no effect on it to any known or significant extent.

(Which of course was of extreme importance in a military way compared with radio-controlled missiles sensitive to enemy jamming.)

The only thing that really affected it was motion. For it was by motion that it "looked within itself to see where it was and where it was going."

All this, as a modern science miracle, had developed within the short span of time from October 1942 when the first successful V-2 belched up from Peenemunde foreshadowing the many which in two years were to drop on London.

The early V-2 rockets had rather primitive guidance and control systems. Yet they had contained what became the very essence of the inertial system: gyroscopes and accelerometers. And not only Newton's Laws had helped deliver the miracle; there had been a French physicist Foucault who developed the first gyroscopic principles, there was a German professor named Schuler who showed how certain gyro-compass errors could be eliminated; as there were others. Later there had been the Peenemunde group who helped develop America's first inertially guided missile, the Redstone (the same which more than a decade afterwards was to send a Holloman chimpanzee as the first of his kind into space). There had also been an American, Charles Draper, who achieved what some guidance experts had called the greatest breakthrough of all with his floated gyros as well as his stable platform (an enlargement of Professor Schuler's own earth-radius-pendulum idea) which was the heart of the free world's first successfully used all-inertial navigation system.

(Draper's demonstration of his system had been a famous one in the annals of guidance history; he had installed all 2,800 pounds of it in a B-29 aircraft at Boston and found his way to Los Angeles without once calling for pilot navigation during the trip.)

But perhaps the oddest thing to find out about the modern guidance miracle was that it stood as the automated end-result of a system used by sea captains for untold generations—dead reckoning.

The immemorial knotted log line trailing from the ship's stern, the trickling sandglass for space-time measurements, the magnetic compass for direction, the sextant for celestial observations, the ship's chronometer (clock) for terrestrial time—all these were a method of inertial guidance (navigation).

Nor were the later electromechanical logs, the radio direction finders, the gyroscopic devices any departure from the basic concept. To get to where he wanted to go the ship's captain had to calculate a given position on the basis of speed, direction, elapsed time, and a known starting point.

The tightly sealed instruments in the inertial guidance system did the same—except that it was all an inside job with even the captain replaced by a computer doing the calculating.

As for the system itself (and there were several to be seen at all times in Holloman's inertial guidance building, carefully sheltered as they were worked on, or conspicuous as glassed models in the museum part of the foyer) any description in less than technical language was another way of making it sound deceptively simple. Though the easiest proof of the opposite was that in a $2 million missile 40% of the cost lay in its guidance system alone (with the rest divided about 30% for airframe, 20% for propulsion, 10% for payload and nose cone).

In its simplest terms, the system consisted essentially of three accelerometers stabilized on a platform by several gyroscopes and provided with a computer. Again the heart of the matter was the accelerometers; in effect nothing more than pendulums pivoted in protective cases to measure changes in motion or acceleration. Three were needed because of three-dimensional motion, east-west, north-south, up-down. The accelerometers worked on the principle of Newton's Third Law of Motion: for every action a reaction.

For instance one's body is an accelerometer when it snaps back during a fast automobile start. So is a weight hung freely on a string in a car. The body lunges backward, the weight swings backward; both sense the motion of the car's acceleration. Thus the three accelerometers mounted in three different axes sensed every motion change and furnished a complete record of such motion from takeoff.

However, the accelerometers also had to "know" the direction they were headed in if the system was to work. This was accomplished by the gyroscopes, usually three in number—which in turn were nothing more than spinning wheels or rotors or spinning masses. (For instance, it was novel to find that the physicists thought of the earth itself as a gyroscope, centered on its axis and pointing always one degree away from the polar star.) The gyroscopes were mounted on the platform (at right angles to each other) to stabilize both the platform and the accelerometers. Spinning in the same three axes, two of them did the stabilizing while the third, acting somewhat like a compass, oriented the platform to a point in space—like the earth toward the polar star.

As for the computer, this acted as the system's integrator. As the changes in motion occurred it started its calculating. Working with an input which included a knowledge of the distance to be covered and the direction of the target, it navigated the missile to the target.

One example of such navigating was related to the way in which an ICBM such as the Minuteman or Titan, in order to reach its target, had to rise, pitch over to its planned trajectory, then cut off its rocket engines, doing each precisely to the fraction of a second. The work of its guidance system therefore was to calculate and accomplish every necessary correction of flight before rocket cutoff, and thus give the missile its proper velocity and exact direction precisely at cutoff time. The system did this by feeding motion information into its computer which in turn directed every on-course adjustment.

As an example of how critical even the slightest error could be—each one-foot-per-second of velocity error could have meant a miss distance of one nautical mile in the target area.

Such in essence then was a missile's inertial guidance system—and in as simplified a form the description could have applied to the flight of an aircraft or spacecraft equipped with an inertial navigation system, which in fact was only another name for the same guidance system but one needing, rather than minutes for its entire journey, hours or days or even longer.

But such a description also left out all the problems. And from the beginning there had been almost too many, in fact for years enough to scout the whole guidance idea as plainly ridiculous. For instance gyro drift, platform gimbaling, accelerometer sensitivity, gravity sensing, component bulk, miniaturization, power requirements, a thousand others, all linked to the one overwhelmingly important main problem: accuracy and reliability.

For the miracle steering was impossible without unbelievable accuracy in the instruments. And though these new gyroscopes were among the most precise instruments ever made by man—no two gyros ever acted or compared exactly alike. So delicate that a finger smudge of dirt or grease could have made it useless, its precision testing to see how it would work was still more precarious. But this was also true of the accelerometers, where a minute error could lose a distant target altogether. So the accelerometer test measurements too had to be exact down to the minuscule fractions of extremely small angles. And thus some models of the latest gyros made to spin in a vacuum, the latest accelerometers small enough to fit in one's hand, and other instruments still more precise are needed to test their performance. It was for these and other reasons that inertial guidance had for a long time been thought utterly impractical. One thing that had helped to revise such ideas had been a whole technological revolution in electronics. Ultra-sensitive detector devices, transistorization, the miniaturizing of instruments—progress along these lines had led the way. Presently there had been many trade-name guidance systems and guidance components, mostly contracted for by the government to fit its long-range missiles and longer-range space plans. And the problems had multiplied.

One place where they were being solved for the Air Force was at Holloman. And the place at Holloman had the imposing title, Central Inertial Guidance Test Facility. In short, CIGTF.

Among the Air Force Systems Command's great laboratories devoted to scientific research and development it was CIGTF which had been created for the sole purpose of teaching our missiles and spacecraft where they should go, or in other words finding their way to a given destination. First established in 1959, it was also the only facility directly charged with the responsibility of wringing out the secrets of inertial guidance systems.

This had come about through a variety of factors. For one thing there had been the Holloman track (and the roaring, snorting, liquid-engine rocket sleds to push whole guidance systems in simulated flight). For another, the advanced data reduction center (and the marvelous computers). Also a huge stratosphere chamber or environmental test chamber to match many conditions of vibration, temperature, humidity, altitude. In time there were two 100-inch centrifuges operating in a part of the main laboratory building, and still later, within its own building, a 260-inch, 30-ton giant, built at a cost of $2½ million, consisting of a massive steel arm that whirled through a 50-foot diameter subjecting accelerometers, gyroscopes, stabilizing platforms, and other inertial guidance parts or entire guidance systems to exactly measured accelerations so perfectly controlled that they could be as gentle as a zephyr or, conversely, run up through successive stresses to as much as 100 G's of restrained brute force. (Actually centrifugal force, which constituted one of the prime test beds for proving guidance system reliability.)

In the huge CIGTF main building there were many smaller, though pricelessly expensive, pieces of test equipment. (Among which a puzzled writer-observer could wander with Carl Roemer or another helpful escort, trying once more to track down a whole assortment of mysteries which could have produced a Kafka-dream of endless dimensions.)

Giant equatorial tables, supported by fluid bearings with a balance so fine that a finger could move a ton weight, were noiselessly producing calibration platform tests. A linear vibrator was subjecting fixed-orientation guidance components to single-plane vibrations as precise as six seconds of arc. A gyro test table supported only by air bearings tested the threshold performance of gyroscopes and, at the same time, their drift characteristics. In a special set of glass-doored ovens many small test items could be seen as they were kept at exactly controlled round-the-clock temperatures to retain their precision qualities. Precision rate tables to determine calibrations of pendulous-type gyros, dividing heads to test accelerometers in a one-G field, optical and electronic support equipment such as autocollimators, theodolites, analog recorders—and many more made up a bewildering variety which (with explanations) at least exposed the utter intricacy of inertial guidance testing even though it did not unveil the mystery.

For in a way the mystery was even deeper. How did one really navigate a spacecraft from the earth to the moon, or through the planetary system, or even beyond? True enough that it may have been part of a problem as old as the first Greek or Phoenician putting out to sea in an open boat, steering "by God and by guess" with many a prayer to old gods like Poseidon. True also that navigation itself had advanced, that seafaring instruments had led the way to space-faring instruments, to a method of feeding motion information into a computer to correct many deviations in space flight. And yet, what of a spacecraft (an Apollo capsule) finding its way exactly and without fail right to the moon?

Certainly this called for the greatest refinements in the navigating system. Or not only in navigating but in controlling large-thrust and very-small-thrust subsystems (of propulsion) in order to follow out the navigating signals. For again it was true that while an ICBM on an earth-bound flight taking a matter of moments might require guidance only during its first or powered phase, a lot more was needed to launch a vehicle into escape-velocity headed unerringly for some deep-space destination.

But perhaps I was merely—confusingly—bringing together two very distinct and separate matters: navigation, and propulsion. For, actually there was another of those deceptively simple answers to the problem of deep-space navigation—so simple indeed that (as in the description of a guidance system itself) it once more sheared away all the true complexity. The "simple" answer was that a space navigating system guided itself by the stars. In other words, inertial guidance had to be improved by means of celestial-inertial guidance—through which celestial information derived from a star tracker would supplement the terrestrial information (derived from an "earth fix") to correct and recorrect deviations in the space vehicle's basic inertial system and thus enable it (with additional propulsion) to reach its true destination.

This indeed was one of the culminating objectives tied into the delicate and expensive CIGTF test equipment and its mission—and it was out of such needs (for more and more refined testing) that still another collection of marvels was designed, created, and finally installed in the CIGTF laboratory (at a cost of $2 million) to become the free world's most advanced test complex for measuring the performance of celestial-inertial guidance systems.

Housed in a sealed, dust-free, glass-and-steel enclosure the guidance engineers liked to call a controlled environmental area, but which was also known as a "clean room" (protected from all outside contamination by air locks, purified inside by filtering systems until "single dustmotes existed almost as in a void"), the new collection of marvels consisted basically of a massive fixture known as a single-star simulator, filled with complicated optics and electronics, a dual-star-and-sky simulator, and a single-axis table on which could be mounted the test item, in other words a star-tracking celestial-inertial guidance system.

A part of the single-star simulator (as I eventually learned) consisted of a unique unit called a monochromator, which was used to "tailor" a star to unbelievable color refinements—to exact wave lengths measured in millimicrons. (One millimicron being equal to one billionth of a meter.)

Other indispensable parts of the system included a spectrophotometer for calibrating simulated star images by astronomical standards, a control console to provide remote settings, a programmer to supply ways of interrogating the tracker during its operation, also various recording instruments, theodolites, power units, thermal conditioners, and support equipment.

All this one could see for oneself by stepping inside a second enclosed area containing the console and the programming and recording equipment, then peering through the heavy glass picture window into the 37-foot-square clean room where the three main structures, the simulators and single-axis table, were situated. But it needed kindly elderly Edgar Godley, the engineer in charge who had spent three decades with the mysteries of optics and navigation (and worked with the U.S. Navy on its Norden bombsight during World War II), to explain what the marvel really was.

For instance the three main structures were positioned on a 100-ton seismic block or gravity-reference fixture isolated from the rest of the concrete building foundation by 18 inches of air space—and so stable and vibration-free that, in terms of inertial guidance testing, it provided a reference base accurate to one second of arc.

"In fact the test complex itself was designed for an over-all accuracy of one second of arc," he said, "and if you want to know how accurate that is—we can use the terms of angular measurements to say that one second of arc is equal to the diameter of a baseball at a distance of ten miles."

Peering through his spectacles as I had peered into the clean room he went on to explain the real mysteries.

"What the guidance system actually has to do in order to get its vehicle to any given destination is to correct its own errors—for instance errors caused by gyro drift. For example a gyro that drifted only five ten-thousandths of a degree in an hour could still miss a lunar target by more than a hundred miles in a fifty-hour flight. The way the celestial-inertial guidance system corrects this drift—and other errors—is by using a star tracker. Basically the tracker consists of an optical window and an optical telescope to sight whatever star it wants to use as a reference point. On the simplest possible terms, this is exactly how navigators have been using the so-called fixed stars in the heavens for centuries. Of course the stars only seem fixed because of being such great distances from the earth. Almost a hundred have been used by mariners ever since seafaring began. However, with our star tracker we have the whole visible sky to choose from—hemispherically at any rate—and with our star simulator we can match over ninety percent of all useable navigational stars. In this way a typical test procedure—as we're doing right now—evaluates the sensors, detectors, scanners, comparators and related instruments of the celestial-inertial system by, first, letting the star tracker acquire a simulated star as its reference point, second, defining the star's position in relation to this reference, and third, monitoring the guidance system as it tracks."

He peered at me more intently through the spectacles and asked a purely rhetorical question—for he answered it himself immediately.

"And why would we create such complex laboratory equipment, do you think, just to simulate a few star positions—instead of taking the star tracker itself outside and using it there? Well, I'll tell you . . . out there the dust and shimmer and atmospheric distortion would simply ruin us. We'd have no true findings at all. Whereas with this celestial-inertial tester we expect to be able to evaluate the next several generations of star trackers and guidance systems for some years to come."

He removed his glasses and polished them as carefully as the equipment of a star tracker.

Like Ed Godley, there were literally scores of Holloman "eggheads" at CIGTF. Both military and civilian, they were engineers, mathematicians, physicists, computer analysts, astronautics experts, experts in optics, technicians, many other kinds of specialists. Generally a colonel headed up the over-all aggregation that gradually swelled to nearly two hundred strong. Tom Oliver who became chief after Bernard Marschner left to fill an Air Force Academy professorate was so deep in blackboard abstractions that the chalk seemed to linger on his fingertips. Later there were other colonels, Bob Savage, Herman Guffey, Len Sugerman, Charles Carson—not only fine engineers but fine scientific managers. And Carl Roemer, a solid professional blessed additionally with that rarest of gifts, scientific eloquence. Major Hal Wright, whose gifts took a different trend, wrote several volumes on test philosophy and advanced guidance system test requirements as well as a brochure to publicize CIGTF throughout the entire technical community. Lieutenants like Forrest Hanvey, Howard McKinley, Francis Mason won Air Force science awards for achievements in both theory and concrete application. There were the civilians too. Gerhard Braun as chief technical consultant and Joachim Gengelbach as chief systems tester were renowned Peenemunde rocketeers. In time their places were filled by other men as brilliant, Congressional appointees like Bill Laubendorfer and Martin Jaenke as consultants, Pete Zagone as chief of test operations. Jack Birge was jack-of-all-trades. Grady Nicholson had mastered all the CIGTF centrifuges. Arthur Abernathy had designed and almost single-handedly gained the laboratory its first stratosphere test chamber. Charlie Bodwell as chief data analyst lived and breathed with computer reports; so did his able assistant Ferdinand ("Fred") Kuhn who was recruited from Germany at a later date by Holloman's chief scientist, Ernst Steinhoff.

(Steinhoff himself was as excellent a scientific manager as he was a scientist, with strings of notable awards; once a leading director at the German Research Center at Peenemunde, a man of restless energy and far-reaching theories, specialist in a wide range of subjects including inertial guidance, electronics, aeronautics, astronautics, physics, meteorology, ballistics, space technology; once also, far back in his youth, the world record holder for free-soaring glider flight and a builder of gliders;

yet still a deceptively youthful-looking man, friendly and genial to meet, with a completely human side that won him as many friends as science projects finding their way to the marvelous test beds at Holloman.)

And in time it was young Fred Kuhn who produced, for CIGTF, another invention as modern as the next day's technology news, an automatic laser beam detector. Though this in turn was only an emergence out of earlier experimentation, by other CIGTF experts; for instance Major Mackey Real who was using one of the latest of all man's weird new inventions, the laser, for still more refined methods of testing the miracle steering of inertial guidance systems.

"We do this," the major told me, "by projecting a laser beam at one end of the Holloman seven-mile test track and aligning it with an inertial guidance system's stabilized platform mounted on a rocket sled at the other end of the track. Because of the laser's intense coherent or monochromatic light we can focus the beam across that distance to an extremely small spot with almost no divergence. We direct the beam through an optical port in the sled structure, onto an attitude-sensing device fixed on the guidance platform. In this way, as the sled blasts along the track at simulated flight velocities, the beam acts as an optical monitor signaling us every motion change in the platform—in other words measuring the platform's pitch, roll, and yaw characteristics more accurately than we were able to measure them before. For this we use a continuous-wave, helium-neon gas laser—though as you might know there are other kinds, for instance ruby rod lasers, some using neodimium crystals to get still other wave-lengths, and so on."

I had heard about lasers of course, as what Hollomanite hadn't after the Gemini 7 capsule's two-week cruise in space when astronauts Borman and Lovell carried a small six-pound laser to flash signals to people at White Sands Missile Range. The experiment never succeeded at White Sands because of cloud overcast, but the orbiting pair did sight a beam flashed up from Hawaii. Since any electromagnetic wave could be transmitted, the Gemini experiment was to consist of a lock-on between a ground-emitted beam and the capsule-emitted beam, and then an attempt to talk over the beam. This idea was in line with some of the newest theories about lasers, which in themselves were so new that the first working model had been built only in 1960. For instance the theory that a single laser beam supported by adequate equipment might carry millions of telephone calls plus any number of radio and TV programs—certainly a remarkable revolution in communications.

Yet this was only one of the laser's miracle-potentials. Its very name gave a clue to others, an acronym built from the first letters of the five key words: Light Amplification by Stimulated Emission of Radiation. Lasers performed their strange marvels in the field of light—but a kind of light never found in nature nor in previous forms of artificial light. Both sunlight and manufactured light, combined of all the colors of the spectrum, became diffused in every direction; it was incoherent light. On the other hand light from a laser consisted of a single color and a single wave-length, emitted through a lens or mirror as a narrow coherent beam so powerful it could travel incredible distances and still hold most of its shape and intensity. One kind called a solid-state laser emitted its beam from a crystal or ruby rod whose chromium atoms were bounced or pulsed into chain reaction (up to billions of pulses a second) by means of a powerful flash lamp coiled around the rod. Another kind called a gas laser derived its beam from a tube filled with any of several kinds of gases whose atomic particles or ions were energized electrically into continuous-wave operation. All this was still coherent light, lens-focused into extraordinary intensity. A laser beam the size of a thin lead pencil, expanded to a foot width by a telescope, could reach the moon without spreading much more than a mile and a half. (The experiment was performed in 1961.) The beam also possessed other properties, for instance a heat potential of thousands of suns, penetration to puncture the hardest substances. Already it had been used as a microsurgical tool in burning away cancer cells, as a welding tool slicing through steel armor plate, as a measuring device more accurate than radar. Besides its use at the Holloman track it had been installed and tested in Holloman aircraft as a range-finding device helping to aim air-launched missiles at their targets. The U.S. Army had developed a crude laser rifle able to shoot "bullets" of hot light—surely the first step to the science-fictioneer's perennial dream of a weapon able to deal out a death ray.

Nevertheless the laser apparatus itself was a completely unimpressive thing to look at—as I discovered when Fred Kuhn led me into a small steel-doored room with its conspicuously posted warning sign: DO NOT ENTER THIS ROOM WHEN RED LIGHTS ARE LIT—LASER TEST IN PROGRESS. No red lights were on when we stepped inside. The laser unit itself was exposed within its long, narrow, metal black box which, during operation, had its cover on. About four feet in length and but a half dozen inches in girth, the box contained nothing more than a neon tube and a couple of mirrors, plus the necessary electronics (trailing wires here and there connected with an ordinary small generator as a power supply) to get the tube lighted.

This was the continuous-wave, helium-neon gas laser being used for the CIGTF inertial guidance track tests. "Basically it's the careful placing of the mirrors about the tube which causes the laser to lase," Fred said. And he added gravely: "Which is a new word itself in the vocabulary of science—that word *lase*. When the ions in a gas laser are energized—or for that matter a ruby rod's chromium atoms—the laser simply *lases*."

The equipment of his automatic laser beam detector was also spread about the room to be worked on—a weird assortment of electrical and mechanical instruments including (he patiently named them for me) an X-Y plotter and an oscilloscope for searching and analyzing operations, a light-sensing element called a photo-diode, an oscillating mirror to move the laser beam during its scanning mode, also microswitches, more generators, a turntable, a remote controller to start the search mode and lock on to the laser beam after it was acquired.

"To call it by its full name," he went on, "it's an automatic laser beam detector and real-time TEM-mode analyzer. The TEM stands for transverse electromagnetic modes, which are characteristic of lasers. You see, with the increase in laser power output, the radiation danger increases. This is especially true where continuous and real-time observing of the laser's TEM modes has to be done, as in our work here. If we wear safety goggles, which make the beam invisible, then we get no real-time observations. With this device however the analysis and optimal tuning of any continuous-wave laser can be done without exposing the investigator to the dangers of looking directly at the laser beam or its reflection. In fact with certain modifications we could also analyze pulsed laser beams, such as ruby lasers emit. And this can all be done in complete safety outside the radiation room."

Tall, stocky, and quiet-voiced, he looked so boyishly pleased with himself that somehow I felt just as pleased for him.

So these were some of the men then—the "eggheads" at CIGTF who helped to shape the destinies of Air Force missiles and spacecraft by taking their miracle steering systems through every simulated condition of space flight with the single exception of weightlessness.

"Though it's not impossible that some day that might come too," said Carl Roemer. "It could be done with what we like to call a guidance evaluation missile. You see, there are really three major test methods for missiles—laboratory, track, and flight. For a long time we've had the first two. The third—by which I mean a recovery-type flight—could be done with an entire guidance system rocketing straight up for a hundred miles, more if necessary, using a two-stage, solid-propellant booster system, reverse thrust to vary its accelerations and separate one kind of guidance error from another, built-in features for attitude and roll control, retro-rockets to slow its free fall and prevent it from burning up in reentry, a stabilizing parachute for spin control and a three-chute system to float the missile and its precious payload safely back to our great range right there behind you if you peer through that window into this magnificently vast and empty desert."

A glowing picture indeed—and put in the inimitably eloquent Roemer manner. After which he had more to say about the CIGTF operation itself.

"But it's not only our evaluation potential—one misses the whole picture unless he knows how we have to brief our customers as to what we can do for them in the A to Z guidance test gamut. For instance every untried component of the guidance system goes on our turntables and shakers or other precision devices. Also out to the test track in sled environments we design ourselves. Also in the stratosphere test chamber which in itself is a great thing to investigate. Then to reduce the raw test data from all these simulated rigors we work hand in glove with the data reduction center. The results come back to our analysis section. Our analyses go into evaluation reports. The reports go back to our customers, the people designing the missiles like Ballistic Systems Division, Space Systems Division, Aeronautical Systems Division. The people building our missiles, like our Air Force contractors. Or to customers like NASA, the National Aeronautics and Space Administration, who need us for their Mercury and Gemini and Apollo capsules too. Which really makes our job something like that of the Consumers Union. In fact our whole mission is to find out for all of them all we can about the one thing that makes inertial guidance systems more than clever heaps of scrap metal—their accuracy and reliability."

And so the guidance mystery also had begun to reveal its secrets. (Leaving out all but the simplifications.) I had seen the shake-table tests, the linear vibrators humming or throbbing or mumbling under their test packages, the shiny dividing-heads doing their precise positioning, the tremendous sled runs with payloads meticulously installed in the great sled forebodies. All of it a most serious operation and a mighty operation. In fact the last kind from which one would expect anything but gravity itself.

But that would have been reckoning without Carl Roemer. And the most unexpected of all revelations took place on another occasion when he rummaged through his desk and pulled out a paper, showing barely any grin at all as he remarked: "Speaking of simplification, we have an excerpt here from a technical report explaining in more simple terms the operation of a typical inertial guidance system."

He flicked the paper, leaned back in his chair, and added: "Not that I'm going to say where this came from, nor from whom. Only that it's collected a slight bit of fame in its own way among our guidance experts—and it might interest you. Therefore I quote."

He quoted.

" 'The missile knows where it is at all times. It knows this because it knows where it isn't. By subtracting where it is from where it isn't, or where it isn't from where it is—depending on which is greater—it obtains a difference or deviation. The inertial guidance system uses deviations to generate corrective commands to drive the missile from a position where it is to a position where it isn't. The missile arrives at the position where it wasn't, consequently the position where it was is now the position where it isn't. In the event that the position where it is now is not the same as the position where it originally wasn't, the system acquires a variation—this variation being the difference between where the missile is and where the missile wasn't. If the variation is considered to be a significant factor, it too may be corrected by the inertial guidance system. However, the missile must now know, also, where it was. The "thought process" of the missile is as follows: because a variation has modified some of the information the missile obtained, the missile is not sure where it was. However, it is sure of where it isn't and it knows where it was. It now subtracts where it should be from where it wasn't—and by differentiating this from the algebraic difference between its deviation and its variation, it obtains the difference called error.' "

Unquote.

And if that wasn't electronic humor—what isn't?

23

STRATO UPROAR

The Herd of Bull Elephants

THE STRATOSPHERE CHAMBER which Carl Roemer had spoken about was one of CIGTF's earlier wonders. If America's first science fiction writer, Poe himself, could have seen it he might have found more to marvel at than the products of his own weird imagination.

Could he have imagined stepping into a massive tomb-like room on earth and in four short minutes "traveling" 140,000 feet above the earth? Or in twenty minutes about 225,000 feet?

Could he have pictured any of his morbid characters leaving their comfortable Fahrenheit environment to congeal like a stick of dry ice at 100 degrees below zero—or boil like a thermal geyser at 200 degrees above?

Could his fertile brain have yielded him the idea of a device in this fabulous chamber (quite as fiendish as any Pit and Pendulum ordeal) that would vibrate him at a force twenty times his own weight—that could "shake the teeth from his head and the bones from his body" if unchecked?

But such parallels shouldn't be pushed too far. Poe's gift for the bizarre was unique in his time. There were others like him. Seventeen centuries before his time a Greek named Lucian was writing about voyages to the moon. Mythical utopias were visited in the imagination of men like Sir Thomas More and Lord Bacon. Poe's contemporary Jules Verne became world famous. Before 1900, H. G. Wells was describing time machines and warring space worlds. And modern science fiction writers had of course outdone science itself, or as one critic, Harold Goodwin, remarked, "had their heroes fighting frozen methane on the planet Jupiter and thinking nothing of cosmic jaunts to Alpha Centauri and beyond."

Actually, if any such writers had stepped into the Holloman chamber within its sand-yellow building opposite the CIGTF building they would have been closer to authentic space travel than chair-begotten fancies could ever have brought them. For that was the chamber's purpose—to simulate outer space flight.

It could match the altitude pressure, temperature, humidity, solar radiation, or vibration conditions to be met by any rocket or missile or high-flying balloon or space craft experiencing real flight. It could match all these things at once. It could match them continuously. Its humidifying steam injectors could form a complete cloud. Or snow. Or frost. Or showers of ice crystals glittering through the chamber's thick-glassed portholes like a scene from Antarctica. It was only a "laboratory" but it could duplicate "weather" anywhere in the world from sea-level to forty miles up.

So not a little awe and shuffling of ghostly feet might have ensued if the ancient space romancers could have watched it at work—provided they remained ghostly enough not to obstruct the men doing the work.

One of the men, Arthur Abernathy, had had so much to do with the chamber's design, specifications, procurement, and actual installing that he probably could have enthused about it even to ghosts.

"We've planned it for aeromedical and space biology tests as much as for missile and inertial guidance tests," he said. "We've had the Holloman chimps inside. Lieutenant McClure was inside before his Manhigh balloon flight. The Stargazer balloon telescope went in before it sailed up for its sky pictures. Missile systems as large as the Falcon or Sidewinder get the full treatment as far up as the ionosphere. And guidance systems get the same."

The very sight of its immense girth and surrounding machinery was impressive enough. Pumps, condensers, air dehydrators, steam and electric generators, compressors, giant valves, as well as a bewildering maze of steel pipes angling in all directions toward the floor, the ceiling, the chamber itself, gave the impression of a king-size engine room in an oceangoing ship.

Within this maze stood the 18-foot-high steel chamber, square and massive and forbidding, with fortress-thick walls more awesome than medieval dungeon walls, inside which could be seen the test area, a space eleven feet deep, eight feet wide, eight feet high, flanked by an anteroom just as high but four feet on each side.

"The anteroom is an air lock," Abernathy went on. "Also a sort of parasite chamber. We can use the anteroom to watch everything inside. Pressure between the two rooms can be equalized in seconds—a doctor can stand in the anteroom ready for anything that happens to his volunteer subjects in the main test room. Both rooms have oxygen regulator outlets, also plug-ins for headsets and microphones. Though, speaking of mikes, we couldn't use them out here." He grinned broadly. "I mean, when the machinery gets going it sounds like a herd of bull elephants out here."

Patting the chamber's steel side as affectionately as he might have patted one of his children, he led me around the corner to its control unit, where some of his handpicked group were readying the panel equipment for another test. For a while he worked busily there himself. But presently, with his chief assistant Clyde Phillips (a typical engineering type with the quiet ways of one who had tended machinery for years) he moved toward the front of the chamber again.

While they talked, a few other men moved in behind, clustering around the front of the chamber. Like a gang of stevedores they were wheeling a low truck on which rested a huge circular cone of metal with countless open receptacles like light sockets, a unit the size of a Thor missile's nose cone.

"This is our new infrared furnace," explained one of them, instrument man Charlie Nichols. "It's a new chamber auxiliary. We designed and built it right here. It can generate up to ninety-five kilowatts. The half-moon shape lets us use it more practically for testing other units at high temperatures."

Slowly, laboriously, with a chain hoist, muscle, brawn, sweat, and some good-natured horseplay, everybody worked to maneuver the huge unit into the main test area and hang it from giant ceiling hooks. Other test equipment was also dragged inside. Through the wide-open front of the chamber the maneuvering was not too difficult.

"That opening was another special design idea," Nichols remarked (as proudly as though it were his own). "The test space inside had to be matched to get the hardware inside. So this eight-by-eight-foot door was put on a sort of monorail, to slide to one side, completely out of the way."

Quiet directions came from Phillips, machinery hummed, metal clanked loudly, and on its smooth monorail the wall of the chamber was slid back into place. Pneumatic cylinders and the force of vacuum pump suction did the rest, sealing it as if no opening had been there at all.

With the muscle work taken care of, most of the group hurried back toward the control unit again.

"For an entire simulated flight we plot a black ink or crayon or tape recorder line which is followed by a light beam along the plotting paper and picked up by a photoelectric cell," said Phillips. "This cell drives the tracking-head up-scale or down. That way we can vary, too. With a little patience we can take the missile or guidance system or balloon package—or for that matter people—right through the realistic flight environment itself."

"For twenty-four hours a day or seven days a week," softly added Nichols. "And man, that's something!"

"That's the herd of wild bull elephants," said Abernathy, smiling.

"He means the noise, not the programming," pointed out Phillips.

Another man in the group, Tom Searcy, standing now at another instrumented cabinet, the automatic data logger, seemed anxious to talk about that.

"Everybody should know what this can do," he said. "It picks up just about everything in the way of environmental data off the recorders, digitizes the stuff, and types it out here at this little old teletypewriter on the table. Why, it doesn't even make the mistakes we do!"

Meanwhile everything had been readied for the new test operation. The talk and banter quieted down. A shrill feedback whistle came from the intercom loudspeaker on top of the chamber as Abernathy tested it. With the feedback cleared he called out technical questions.

"Anteroom door closed? Chamber door closed? Air pressure on? Ready for the pumps? Okay—now for the herd of wild bull elephants!"

As a final joke it was evidently a standing feature.

And suddenly the elephants came—in a way that would have scared even ghosts out of their ectoplasmic skins. A roar like a score of freight trains, broader than a jet roar, then high-pitched and screaming, mixed with ear-splitting bangs of metal, clanks, thumps, the hiss of altitude regulators, battering of pumps and pistons, shrill whine of compressors, a din, a bedlam, a discord that grew and grew, sustained, deafening, a racket that seemed infernal.

Though it lifted no man there out of his skin. Nor did it shake the building or the massive chamber itself. Against its pandemonium the red and green control panel lights blinked silently; soundlessly every stylus ran across its program paper; the teletypewriter began writing to itself in its own semighostly way.

A long time later the bedlam was still going on. By which time most of the operating crew had gone elsewhere leaving only two lonely sentinels, in this instance tall quiet Clyde Phillips and instrument man Nichols. Both of whom seemed stoically inured to this cacophonous side of science.

But if there really had been any ghosts, it seemed a safe bet they had gone wearily away too.

24

AERIAL WARFARE

Electronic Hare-and-Hounds

No, THE GLAMOUR OF SCIENCE was not the stertorous breathing of a stratochamber under an agony of controlled bedlam, nor the protesting grumbles of metal tortured by linear shakers, nor people peering at every inch of magnetic tape spread along a thirty-foot table. As our crew-cut colonel had said, the glamour was chimpanzees blasting into orbit under the world's eyes, rockets roaring along a test track, intrepid balloonists daring fringe-of-space hazards, pilots going every day on their dangerous tests and maneuvers.

Yet what was "glamour" even? Who could really define it? If it had anything to do with excitement there was the fact that men were intensely excited locked away in their research rooms or in test laboratories or immersed in a sea of abstractions working out their theories, equations, mathematical formulas, or poring over tissue slides, or studying stress relationships between sine waves and square waves. Some even acknowledged as much when they were asked—though in rather puzzled tones, to be sure. (As if wondering what the questioner would think up next.)

And so the glamour really was what anyone wanted to make of it— that x of man's interior searchings that kept him as rapt for endless hours scanning cosmic ray data through a microscope as an astronaut in a space capsule beholding the cosmic scene itself. Perhaps the real clue lay in the existence of dedicated men, living an idea, a dream, an action at the height of their powers and mental and emotional drives no matter what the shape or form. For there were as many of that kind in the laboratories and test areas as in the tests. And certainly plenty at Holloman.

Take a man named Woehl for example. Walter Woehl was another of the "quiet" men in the data building, though not in the data reduction activity. Later they moved him to a building of his own—and in fact that's part of the story.

The Woehl kind of glamour was physics. Born in Germany, he had majored in applied physics and optics at Berlin's Technical University. He also began his professional career there. Later he was deputy director of the German Air Force's ballistic institute at Berlin-Gatow, then chief optical physicist at a similar institute in Braunschweig. Going to England after the war he became chief consulting physicist at the Royal Arsenal for the British Ministry of Supply, and from there came directly to Holloman to be in charge of developing and testing advanced optical instrumentation—which was as important in tracking missiles and space objects as eyes would have been to the blind.

The force of dedication in this slender, sun-tanned man (who was good enough a swimmer to be asked to coach the small fry in Alamogordo's municipal pool) was such that as often as not the large fluorescent lamps over his desk were still lighted at midnight and the light in his mind had filled scratch pads and drafting paper with endless designs and calculations in the realm of theoretical and applied optics.

Out of the designs and calculations came a camera system unique in the missile world—the Facet-Eye.

Its uniqueness (when it was finally built and installed in a 24-foot dust-proof astrodome in the North Area where a small instrumentation-equipped building nearby became the new place to find Walter Woehl almost any time) consisted of twenty-four five-inch refracting telescopes as long as the barrels of an antiaircraft gun, and one shorter telescope, all squared on a gimbaled support between a U like a giant gun mount, and linked to twenty-five TV-like image-orthicon tubes which displayed their images on the same number of oscilloscope screens inside the building arranged both for direct scanning and photographic reproduction.

With the snow-white astrodome roof peeled back for action and the massive but delicately balanced tracking mount swinging all the barrels into position at once, the resemblance to an exaggerated antiaircraft gun was complete.

Yet it was not that warlike a creation. For the tryout tests by its hard-working inventor it was trained on planetary bodies. This in itself was unique, for the tests were made in broad daylight and the objects (at least to the naked eye) could not even be seen. Yet with the proper sidereal calculations and while its seven-ton four-axis tracking mount moved at a sidereal rate, the new giant among camera systems proved itself by capturing continuous bright-image views, first of Venus, then of Jupiter.

Simultaneously with the tracking operation the images were transmitted to the cathode-ray oscilloscope tubes indoors where a small but highly official group of Holloman people witnessed the success of the event as they clustered near the display console with its banks of tiny TV-like viewing screens and voiced comments that indicated their own kind of quiet or excited professional interest.

The real success was demonstrated a few hours later when photographs made by the 8 x 10 precision-plate view camera showed distortion-free Venusian and Jupiterian images of a clarity and intensity previously possible only during night hours—and over a total field many times the size obtained by standard tracking telescopes.

In terms of daylight star detection this improved tracking represented an advance of about six stellar magnitudes.

Also in scanning the heavens that same night, photos of the Pleiades cluster made in snapshot-time showed image sensitivity reaching faint stars up to the twelfth magnitude.

Still later the Facet-Eye tracked one of America's satellites, Discoverer XXV, with such success that the film record of the event was used in a national TV news broadcast.

So the theories and calculations had worked, and the long day-and-night hours spent far from the tumult of the launch pads and firing ranges had brought forth their own product that was not a little glamorous even to watch.

Nevertheless that wasn't the way the Facet-Eye's originator regarded it. Basically, it turned out, the Facet-Eye had been conceived for the purpose of tracking missiles as well as satellites and other space vehicles.

He gave a technical description of the Facet-Eye operation.

"The twenty-five individual camera chains work simultaneously from common rack equipment. Each chain but one has its seventy-five-inch focal-length telescope, image-orthicon camera, camera control unit, video amplifying link, and reproducing display unit. The twenty-fifth chain—you may have noticed its telescope is shorter than the others— is for wide-angle viewing. Each telescopic field is very small, only fifty-two minutes of arc, to capture daylight images. However, by combining all these viewing fields in a kind of mosaic pattern we get a total field of two and a half by seven degrees, and get the same accuracy optically as with a ballistic camera of like quality."

He also spoke about the tracking mount.

"It was made especially to take the twenty-five camera units and give us complete tracking flexibility by its altitude-azimuth and equatorial mechanisms. The astrodome has been fully synchronized too—it's an integral part of the system. In fact because of our new filter techniques there's another thing—we're providing our missile analysts here with real-time readouts of target coordinates. In other words the system can sense and present in digital form so the data can be stored or taped on any memory device used by the Holloman computers. This means the Facet-Eye can be used for special missile detection as well as for intelligence and other such purposes."

Still speaking quietly and like an essentially peace-loving person (which was the whole impression one got of Walter Woehl's real nature) he seemed the living example of a man as satisfied with what he was doing as other men doing more spectacular things.

And then there were the more spectacular things again—and other dedicated men. For instance the Facet-Eye itself might have been used to sight some odd-looking aerial maneuvers that had long been going on (though in brief daily flights) high in the skies over Holloman.

The telescopes (with their one-mile minimal focusing distance) could have fixed on a two-motored cargo plane with the familiar USAF on its round cigar-shaped fuselage. The plane was just tooling along. Then it banked sharply, turned, held to its new course—and seemed barely to get out of the way of a slim needle-nosed jet craft with brilliant orange colors which streaked across its wake like a supersonic arrow.

As swiftly, the orange plane disappeared in a mass of fluffy white cloud on the other side of the unwieldy cargo plane. But it appeared again, sliding into view with sinister speed, and again darted past the slower plane before skimming into the opposite cloud bank.

Still a third time this happened. To a ground observer with a telescope it might have seemed that the two aircraft, one so cumbersome, one so sleek, were playing games with each other. And in a way, they were. For it was an electronic game—and to an interested spectator within the big unwieldy cargo plane instead of on the ground the game was much more exciting.

(I was that spectator and I was excited.)

For instance there was the stripped-down belly section of the plane with its specially installed instruments, where bright green lights pulsed like waves across one viewing scope and danced like spray up and down another. The bright green lights were pulse frequencies, picked up from the bright orange jet craft slipping through the clouds outside.

And there was the jet itself, an F-106 Delta Dart, now carrying a deadly GAR missile, a guided air rocket—not, of course, to be actually launched at its ponderous C-131 target but looking deadly just the same —and equipped with other special instruments that would tell whether it was scoring "hits" or not.

So it was really a game—of hide-and-seek, hunt-and-escape, hare-and-hounds, all for the purpose of simulating one of the most dangerous activities ever devised by man in his long and troubled history: aerial warfare.

The viewing scopes in the C-131 were pulse and frequency spectrum analyzers. The instruments were electronic countermeasures equipment—some called it missile countermeasures equipment—familiarly known as ECM or MCM devices. In aerial warfare like the game now going on, ECM represented the art of jamming and confusing the flight of enemy missiles and aircraft making it impossible for them to lock-on or find their true targets.

At the rear of the C-131 behind the steel-and-aluminum frames of the detection and jamming instruments was another ECM device, a large heavy metal box, bolted to the floor, separately pressurized, vented on the outside underneath the aircraft like a miniature bomb bay—actually a chaff dispenser.

The chaff was tinfoil. Thousands of tiny fluttery strips of it. An innovation first used during the London blitz in World War II, now a standard passive jamming device (meaning with no electromagnetic radiation of its own) to be released into the airstream, confusing enemy radar scopes by creating an effect of false targets, something like a smoke screen with glittering tinfoil as the smoke.

And here were the dedicated men again—perhaps not as intensely single-minded as a Walter Woehl burning his lonely lamps night after night, but intent enough just the same. The pilot, Major Bill Romansky, whipping his crate of an aircraft around as though it were a T-33 trainer. The ECM chief, Captain Bill Marr, scanning the skies outside through the small glass-domed escape hatch overhead. Staff Sergeant Arthur Plumstead operating the viewing scopes. Airman Bill Goble at the power supply channels. Airmen Dick Linders and Lewis Hill working the chaff dispenser. All of them wearing their intercom headsets, talking occasionally, checking other instruments.

Trailing his long headset cord behind him Captain Marr moved back toward the pressure box where Linders and Hill were ejecting small packets of chaff along a traveling belt assembly; then returned and hovered by the viewing scopes. The bright green scope lights raced evenly as they picked up the F-106 pulses.

Then the F-106 was coming in again. Marr spoke sharply. Panel switches were pushed. The ECM jamming transmitters were snapped into action. For another few seconds the bright green lights raced—and then exploded in a shower of green sparks, blurring everything on the scope.

"It's still working!" someone said softly.

They all grinned.

It was almost like being in actual combat, there was the definite feeling of being hunted—and of escaping. (Perhaps some were thinking also of the Air National Guard missile that had gotten loose once over these same skies, creating havoc against its bomber-target.)

The tension was almost the same.

But while the maneuvers still went on, ECM expert Marr performed his own quiet explaining.

"Basically what we're doing is testing the vulnerability of Air Force guided missiles. Any radio or radar or infrared guided missile can be jammed—all but the true ballistic missiles, the long-range ICBM's that have their own inertial guidance systems which aren't affected by electromagnetic radiation. As for the rest, anything that can be done with one radio wave can be undone with another—that's the theory. ECM does its best to prove this theory. It's also safe to assume that our potential enemies in the world, if any" (his eyes twinkled but his face remained serious), "are busy perfecting their own ECM hardware. Jamming our Voice of America broadcasts overseas is one example."

I had seen as much for myself overseas, in the Munich station.

"But by finding out our own vulnerability," he went on, "we let our missile people develop still better missile equipment, in other words what we call counter-countermeasures, or ECCM. For instance we install an oscillograph instead of a warhead in the missile—like that GAR missile under the F-106 out there now—and collect the performance data, such as antenna position, pitch, yaw, error signals, automatic gain control, in short how well the missile itself is performing against us. Actually the F-106 out there is flying the profile the missile itself would take in free flight. The proof of the pudding also is in our live firings. That is against drone targets," he smiled again "with ECM black boxes in the drone launch aircraft to complete the simulated environment. The jamming equipment can be turned on and off and the frequencies tuned up or down through the drone's electronic control link. Chaff-dispensing pods can also be electronically controlled on the drone aircraft. So can pyrotechnic-dispensing pods which are used with missile systems depending on infrared guidance. In fact there's a whole bag of ECM tricks—primarily divided between what we call deceptive and brute-force devices. And the bag is always changing . . ."

He was talking as quietly as Walter Woehl himself talked, and in a way as eloquently. The ECM devices were Captain William Marr's glamour as physics and facet-eye calculations were the Woehl kind.

And weren't both as fascinating as—say the activities of chimpanzees?

25

EPILOGUE

Reaching for the Stars

THE STREETS OF ALAMOGORDO were cool streets in the early morning, before the sun tipped its golden lances over the eastern hills, and quiet streets before the cars leaving countless driveways formed a steady stream along Pennsylvania Avenue to roll onward toward the great missile base. After that seven o'clock exodus there would be another brief lull, the wide streets almost empty again, occasional house-wives in wraparounds bending over their shrubberies, or sprinkling the lawns wrenched out of desert real estate . . . long shadows still angling from young elms and cottonwoods and graceful willows which were slowly making the city greener year by year. In the downtown area in the cool of morning the shops looked shadowy too, full of wearing apparel, TV consoles, household appliances, living-room suites, refrigerators, photo equipment, books, beauty adornments, all the paraphernalia of living which later in the day would create the shopping bustle by the same housewives. The White Sands and Sierra theatre marquees across the street from each other displayed the latest Hollywood posters. The fine new city hall with its wide parking squares looked deserted except for a few police cars. The Plaza Cafe and the Wagon Wheel held a few early breakfast patrons. The Rolland drug store, Penney's and Woolworth's, Western Auto and Firestone, the Inkwell, Gamble's, Hughen's Music Center, Southwestern Book Shop, Brunell Dress Shop, the Western Union office, Tom Charles Insurance Agency, Safeway and Food Mart stores, shops for jewelry and shoes and hardware . . . all had the quiet aspect of places solidly a part of the town's economic life. As a comparative newcomer in their midst the emporium-sized Yucca News Stand presided over by Paul and Sylvia Varner stood foursquare on the main street; favorite lounging place for the Holloman eggheads and bookworms, where every paperback from *G-String Murders* to *Elements of Calculus* was on display, also hardcover volumes, reference works, language books, domestic and foreign newspapers, domestic and foreign magazines . . . a natural magnet for the town's *cognoscenti* who also hailed from so many far-off places.

Behind the shopping sections the broad flat streets stretched all the way back to the hills again.

How strange it had all looked to me at first, fresh from the lush contrasts of Europe—and now how difficult to recapture even the sense of those initial impressions after having seen, inspected, and catalogued the picture a thousand times. The curiosity over new sights and places had been like the curiosity about Holloman . . . the newness of "place" was always interesting, and the challenge in subtle ways the same. The years in between had been fascinating years, filled indeed with the fervor of learning the Air Force story—all this magnificent part of it going on just beyond the city. How much that newness had contributed to the thrill of watching missiles vaulting into the blue, balloons rising to the stratosphere, drones playing tag in the skies, rocket sleds dashing along a track, chimps performing their sophisticated antics. And to the admiration for the men planning and performing the deeds, the inspired "makers and doers" of Holloman. Was the wonder still as fresh after so many viewings? Was it time to move on, looking for new matters to trap the senses and swing the imagination?

But whether I stayed or went, there were certain things clear to me. One: the admiration for the *people* of Holloman would remain the same. Two: the deeds they were performing and would perform remained just as wondrous. Three: there would always be new deeds and new advances, the end was not even remotely in sight. And four (the real sticker, deflating the questioner as neatly as the question): the brimming fullness of Holloman deeds would never be written.

At least not in any book, such as this one. Hadn't the impossibility been mentioned in the very beginning? But then it had been theory—now it had turned out to be true. Like a Herodotus rather than a Thucydides full of painstaking completeness one could delve into certain events, examine certain features, talk with countless people and come up with a part of the story or partial answers—fragmentary for each event, equally so for the whole. Perhaps some of the uniqueness had been caught. (And there was always the pleasure of writing the stories.) But to report all the Holloman happenings in one book . . .

There were also the new things beginning to happen. Since manned space flight was already succeeding and certainly would go on to explore the moon and perhaps some of the planets, many steps on the way to that series of great events had already been started. But many others lay just around the corner. The state-of-the-art had been advancing— flights would soon be orbiting the earth in the first man-operated craft, deep space probes would learn more about the moon landings, attempt soft impacts on Mars and Venus, experiment still further with space rendezvous problems, plot Gemini and Apollo flights to carry new astronauts and space crews farther than ever into the void. Gemini-Titan static tests had been completed at contractor plants, Apollo-Saturn guidance tests at Holloman itself. Spacecraft landing-gear tests had also been carried out at Holloman—again using the famous captive missile test track. And there were other ways in which Holloman had become (and would be) more important to man's greatest adventure, that of lifting himself into space and exploring space.

For instance one of its largest and most far-reaching undertakings was involved with the ABRES (Advanced Ballistic Reentry Systems) program—the Air Force Systems Command's multibillion dollar project to study missile and spacecraft reentry phenomena in relation to military uses.

Such programs by their very nature extended through a mesh of complex research tasks at many different research sites. The Holloman part in ABRES tied directly into the range: to fly and study the reentry vehicles themselves.

This had called for new second-generation tracking radar (to distinguish and identify live warheads from decoys), a whole new data reduction center (for the astronomical amount of signature data that would have to be processed), more working room, more people, more refined equipment (the new computer, new data sensors, a costly microdensitometer to help measure reentry facts and an even more expensive clean room to house such items).

But above all it had called for an expanded concept of overland launching and inland recovery, which had started long before with Matador and Mace missiles flying the Wendover corridor from Wendover Air Base, Utah, to White Sands; had continued with the Air Force's Hound Dog missiles launched toward the range from points in Texas;

then the Army's Sergeant missiles launched from Datil, New Mexico; and was progressing still further with both Army and Air Force missiles such as the Pershing and Athena flying in from launch sites as far away as Utah again. In fact, as one of Holloman's chief civilian consultants for range matters, Orvie A. Steele, put it, "With the ABRES program Holloman really got into the ICBM business. As far as the range is concerned it's the most significant program we've ever had."

Likewise there were the more diverse signs of Holloman growth. One of its newest commanders, Brigadier General Leo A. Kiley, who took over late in 1965 after the long and distinguished career of Colonel Ralph S. Garman, emphasized as much when he said:

"We're now the focal point in the entire Department of Defense for testing inertial guidance equipment for aircraft and missiles for the Army, Navy, and Air Force. We have one of the most unique test facilities in the world in our seven-mile-long track. We test items such as nose cones for the most advanced ballistic missiles, parachute ejection systems for the most advanced aircraft. In our aircraft test organization we're performing tests on the most advanced aircraft in the inventory, the RF-4C and F-4D . . ."

And there were other facts. For example some $19 million worth of new radars had been built and installed on the range to support the new missile and reentry studies. Located at various sites to allow both side-view and head-on tracking of reentry bodies, they represented some of the most remarkable tracking equipment to be found in the space world. One part of this measuring complex called Ratscat (Radar Target Scatter Site) was a static-type facility which collected radar reflectivity measurements on full-size and scale reentry vehicles, decoys, and aerospace craft. Another called the Rampart site (the "Rampart" meant Radar Advanced Measuring Program for Analysis of Reentry Techniques—a ponderous jawbreaker even the space engineers shied at spelling out too frequently) was really the heart of the new data acquisition system, with a towering 60-foot dish antenna supported on a 95-ton concrete pedestal and radiating a pencil beam possessing a peak power of 24 million watts—enough to trace an object the size of a basketball more than a thousand miles out in space. The Rampart radar's ultra-narrow beam traced the path of various missiles and their payloads plummeting toward the range at reentry speeds and collected the measurements that made up the missiles' identifying radar signatures. Its high-speed tracking and data processing units accepted more than a hundred such measurements during each second of flight and could also differentiate with uncanny accuracy between various reentry payloads so as to distinguish one from the other.

In addition to the new radars had come other new facilities. One of these was known as the ABRES film laboratory, which formed a link between the radar-tracking and data-reduction activities. Since one of the ABRES program objectives was "to acquire missile identity data and performance characteristics through electronic pulse signals recorded on film and fed through computers for detailed analysis," the new film laboratory, installed at a cost of more than a million dollars, both supplied and processed the hundreds of thousands of feet of high-speed film that was produced from every missile reentry flight.

In turn this had called for another one-of-its-kind space age tool—described as a programmable film reader after it was installed at the data reduction center for about a quarter of a million dollars. The film reader collected the flying missiles' electronic signatures. This was, to say the least, a complicated procedure. The signature or "electronic identity" of the missile was derived from its characteristic pattern of reflected radar pulses, such as could be viewed on a radar or oscilloscope screen. For example, the radar sent out a pulse, the pulse was reflected back from the target, and its changed shape helped to determine what the target or missile actually looked like. By using optical projection and electronic-beam scanning this novel new "reader" was able to pick off these pulse coordinates in series of graphs and feed them into a computer. The computer then digitized them for human inspection and analysis. (Or in fact stored them on magnetic tape for comparison with characteristic signature data from other missiles.)

Such, then, had been some of the newest increments in the Holloman growth picture. By 1966 the total annual cost of operating these vast holdings had risen to $75 million. The total annual payroll was over $50 million. Almost 9,000 working people were then crowding the buildings and facilities where, a short two decades before, had been nothing but a few tents and quonset huts. The growth had come about not only through the ABRES program but because of so many advances that were always materializing in the space and science world itself—of which ABRES was a part, so that it too would only be leading to new things, events, happenings, breakthroughs in the dream of man to chart his way through the stars. And perhaps if a writer had felt that he had to search more carefully for such evidences, it was only a case after all of being too near the forest to see every tree.

For still the clues kept coming.

"Now that we've installed the new hardware—the microdensitometer and the computers and other equipment—we're ready for a great deal more in our reentry quest," said Herb Barker (by this time a lieutenant colonel). "Some of our new data sensors are so advanced they're not even duplicated elsewhere in the Air Force inventory. The clean room and its equipment also includes special film processing units to make refined density measurements. The sensors are used locally with the new radar at our Rampart site. Also with White Sands FPS-16 radars—controlled in real-time through their data center and connected there through our own data links."

"The CDC 3600 computer is being still further improved," said Robert Tantzen, "so we'll have no trouble keeping up with the state of the art. The new microdensitometer analyzes missile data for studies in reentry physics. And it produces a digital tape in IBM format for direct playing into the computer."

"The new microdensitometer," said Walter Woehl, "is a very high-precision instrument—it cost the Government over half a million dollars—which reads and measures photo densities on films and plates by application of a fine light-line projected through the emulsion by microscopic optics and onto a photo cell to measure the intensity and attenuation of light in the emulsion. This is needed for our reentry analyses and takes place after the data reach us from the Rampart tracking site."

"Our Rampart site," it was Orvie Steele speaking again, "is now bringing us a bagful of identification signatures. This goes for every type of reentry vehicle heading our way, just as it would if—Heaven forbid—they were enemy missiles. For instance the way we're tracking our four-stage Athena missiles flying in from Green River, Utah. The way the system works is this: each flight is an up-and-over trajectory with a reentry velocity of about sixteen thousand miles and a reentry altitude of nearly fifty miles. We have real-time command of the missile at all times. The radars are slaved together and the data fed into the computers. The first and second stage boosters detach toward selected off-range safety areas, the third and fourth stages along with the payload land on the range itself. As you can see, we're doing this with our latest tracking equipment and the help of the whole White Sands Missile Range—just as it could be done if some hard traveling space crew ever whizzed our way hailing us with a long 'Earth ho!'"

So all this was reflected in the growth and advancement of Holloman.

And for a curious observer scurrying out to get the story, instead of a balloon rising through the troposphere and then coming down with a McClure or Joe Kittinger to be met and asked questions, the story would be a part of these farther happenings, whatever they were to be, of men exploring still deeper in the void, full of the sound and tumult of such going, involved in the most eerie, exciting, scarcely creditable experiences ever written into the history of man, which everyone in the wide world would be waiting to hear.

APPENDICES

APPENDIX A

A Brief History of Holloman Air Force Base

HOLLOMAN AIR FORCE BASE, the home of the Air Force Missile Development Center, is located in the Tularosa Basin ten miles west of Alamogordo in south-central New Mexico. To the east tower the 9,000-foot Sacramento Mountains and to the west lie the 6,000-foot San Andres Mountains. Construction here began on February 6, 1942, with the original intention of forming a training site for the British Overseas Training Program. Operationally baptized as the Alamogordo Bombing and Gunnery Range, the site was elevated to full Army Air Base status within a few months and known as Alamogordo Army Air Field.

As early as 1943 the unique facilities and physical environment of this isolated installation were considered for a guided missile research and development program. No effort, however, was made to interfere with the program of training heavy bomber crews which was then in force; and instead, the facilities at Wendover, Utah, were ultimately selected for this early work which later became the central theme of the AFMDC mission.

It was in the northwestern corner of the air field bombing range that man saw the first atomic bomb explosion, on July 16, 1945.

With the cessation of World War II hostilities the Alamogordo Army Air Field was inactivated and all but forgotten in the postwar planning until the latter part of 1946. Because the old bombing range still afforded an immediately available area 38 miles wide and 64 miles long, it was selected as the Air Force's Guided Missile Test Range. Responsibility for reactivating the base was delegated to the Air Materiel Command, and in March 1947 a detachment led by Colonel Paul F. Helmick arrived and made preparations for the start of the new mission. As the Air Materiel Command people evacuated the Wendover base and moved to the vast Tularosa Basin, they brought as part of their physical and intellectual baggage a major portion of the embryonic

Air Force guided missile program. The first rocket was launched at Holloman on July 23, 1947.

Shortly after the Air Force became a separate branch of service, Alamogordo Army Air Field was renamed Holloman Air Force Base in honor of Colonel George V. Holloman, a pioneer in military technical research and development. In April 1951 the base became a part of the newly formed Air Research and Development Command with the designation of 6540th Missile Test Wing. At first it was a satellite to the Air Force Missile Test Center at Patrick Air Force Base, Florida, but became a separate center in September 1952 with the designation 6580th Missile Test Wing. It became Holloman Air Development Center on October 10, 1952, and was designated a permanent Air Force installation, still forming a part of the Air Research and Development Command. On September 1, 1957, the Holloman Air Development Center was redesignated the Air Force Missile Development Center, and on April 1, 1961, the Air Research and Development Command was redesignated the Air Force Systems Command.

During the time the base was being reactivated in 1947, Army Ordnance was building White Sands Proving Ground, which had its range just to the south of the Holloman range. At first the two installations worked together informally, scheduling their missions for the most efficient use of the combined range, an area 100 miles long by 40 miles wide. In 1952 this combined operation was formally named the Integrated White Sands Range operation and placed under Army management, with the use of the range coordinated by an Army, Navy, and Air Force committee. At present the range is known as White Sands Missile Range and is administered as one of three national ranges by the Department of Defense, supporting missile test programs of the Army, Navy, Air Force, National Aeronautics and Space Administration, and other government agencies.

APPENDIX B

Air Force Missile Development Center Commanders

Colonel Don R. Ostrander: 8 June 1952 to 24 September 1954.
Major General Leighton I. Davis: 25 September 1954 to 2 July 1958.
Major General Daniel E. Hooks: 3 July 1958 to 14 September 1960.
Colonel Ralph S. Garman: 14 September 1960 to 22 September 1960.

Major General William M. Canterbury: 23 September 1960 to 20 July 1961.

Colonel Ralph S. Garman: 21 July 1961 to 31 October 1965.

Brigadier General Leo A. Kiley: 1 November 1965 to —.

Holloman Base Commanders

Colonel Louie P. Turner: 26 November 1942 to 5 June 1943.

Lt. Colonel Oscar L. Beal: 6 June 1943 to 25 August 1943.

Lt. Colonel Glen M. Pike: 26 August 1943 to 26 November 1943.

Lt. Colonel Frank B. Bostrom: 27 November 1943 to 20 April 1944.

Colonel Roscoe C. Wriston: 11 April 1944 to 29 December 1944.

Colonel John W. Warren: 30 December 1944 to 25 June 1945.

Colonel William O. Eareckson: 26 June 1945 to 2 August 1945.

Colonel Maurice A. Preston: 3 August 1945 to 2 October 1945.

Colonel Kermit D. Stevens: 3 October 1945 to 21 August 1946.

Colonel Tomla W. Inlay: 22 August 1946 to 15 March 1947.

Colonel Paul F. Helmick: 16 March 1947 to 25 August 1949.

Colonel William F. Baynes: 26 August 1949 to 7 June 1952.

Colonel Don R. Ostrander: 8 June 1952 to 30 September 1953.

Colonel Frank D. Sharp: 1 October 1953 to 4 July 1955.

Colonel Thomas C. Kelley: 5 July 1955 to 5 March 1958.

Colonel James A. McKerley: 6 March 1958 to 6 June 1960.

Lt. Colonel Lee F. Peterson: 7 June 1960 to 1 July 1960.

Colonel Robert S. Maloney: 2 July 1960 to 19 August 1960.

Colonel Edward C. Tates: 20 August 1960 to 3 November 1961.

Lt. Colonel Dean D. Cunard: 4 November 1961 to 23 July 1962.

Lt. Colonel Emanuel F. Bonvicin: 24 July 1962 to 30 April 1963.

Colonel Henry C. Godman: 30 April 1963 to 1 June 1965.

Colonel Alden G. Thompson: 1 June 1965 to 30 June 1965.

Colonel Robert M. Caldwell: 1 July 1965 to —.

APPENDIX C

The First Atomic Bomb

THE FIRST ATOMIC TEST OPERATION, known as Project Trinity, took place on the morning of Monday, July 16, 1945, in the north-central portion of the Alamogordo Bombing and Gunnery Range.

Headquarters of the Bombing and Gunnery Range was located at Alamogordo Army Air Field, known since 1948 as Holloman Air Force Base; but the explosion site was actually nearer the town of Carrizozo, about thirty miles away, than to Alamogordo, New Mexico, which was sixty miles distant.

This particular site was chosen for reasons of both safety and security. It was in a region of public grazing land that had always been sparsely populated and was now less populated than ever since being withdrawn by the War Department for use as a bombing range. Preparations for the test explosion began in earnest four days prior to July 16, with an old ranch house situated on the range serving as base of operations. The bomb was placed on top of a steel detonation tower on Saturday, July 14, and installation of the detonation mechanism was then started. Meanwhile, other technicians went about installing seismograph equipment at varying distances from the tower location, which was designated Zero. Other instrumentation was set up for recording temperature, air pressure, and similar data wanted by the project scientists.

Three observation points were established at 5.7 miles each from Zero. These were wooden shelters protected by cement and earthen barricades. The observation point lying south of the bomb tower served as a control center, where Dr. J. Robert Oppenheimer, head of Los Alamos Scientific Laboratory, was to take his position. A fourth post was at the base camp, ten miles from Zero, and a fifth on a mountainside twenty miles distant. Most of the scientists and "visiting firemen" present at the test were stationed at this last post; among them Dr. Knox Millsaps, later Chief Scientist of the Air Force Missile Development Center.

The test was originally set for four o'clock on the morning of July 16, but rain and lightning early that morning caused it to be postponed until five-thirty. The bomb could not be exploded under rainy conditions because rain would increase the danger from radioactive fallout, as well as interfering with observations of the test. However, the rain stopped about four o'clock, and at five-thirty the bomb was exploded successfully. In the view of most observers, the brilliance of the light from the explosion—necessarily watched through dark glasses—overshadowed the shock wave and sound that arrived some seconds later. But the shock still knocked over two men at one of the inner observation posts.

Immediately after the test, two lead-lined tanks went forth to explore the site with measuring instruments and to scoop up samples of material from the ground. The bomb tower had virtually disappeared, and in its place was a crater about 400 yards in diameter and fifteen feet deep. Sands in the crater were fused to a glasslike solid the color of jade. This substance has sometimes been referred to as "trinitite," after the code name Project Trinity, which has also given the name Trinity Site to the actual explosion point.

Although no information on the test was released until after the atomic bomb was used as a weapon against Japan, people in surrounding areas were quite aware that something special had happened in the early morning of July 16. The light flash and the thunder clap made a vivid impression over a radius of roughly 160 miles. Glass was shattered 120 miles away in Silver City, New Mexico. And Chicago newspapers carried an item on the explosion of a munitions dump somewhere in New Mexico.

There was considerable excitement in New Mexico later in the year over the discovery of cattle with curiously spotted hide and hair, apparently as a result of fallout from the atom test. But the site itself was kept off limits to the public until September 1953, when a throng estimated at between six and seven hundred persons came for a first public showing of Trinity Site. By this time the danger of radiation at the site had subsided; and similar visits have been arranged at various intervals since then. However, the site is still restricted, if only because it still lies within a military test range. In effect, the Alamogordo Bombing and Gunnery Range was transformed after the war into an Air Force guided missile test range, which in turn was combined in September 1952 with adjacent Army ranges to form the interservice White Sands Missile Range.

BIBLIOGRAPHY

Abbreviations used in this section:

PDC. Prevention of Deterioration Center.
AFMDC-TN. Air Force Missile Development Center—Technical Note.
AFMDC-TR. Air Force Missile Development Center—Technical Report.
ARL-TDR. Aeromedical Research Laboratory—Technical Documentary Report.
MDC-TDR. Missile Development Center—Technical Documentary Report.
WP-MDSGD. Working Paper—Central Inertial Guidance Test Facility.
ASTIA. Armed Services Technical Information Agency.

Published in scientific journals:

Abernathy, A. H. Jr. "Missile Testing and Environmental Chambers." *PDC Newsletter*, National Research Council, Vol. III, No. 3, April 1960, pp. 1,2.

————, and J. S. Byrd. "Development and Application of Controlled Vibration Testing." *Holloman Monthly News Bulletin*, American Rocket Society, Vol. 5, No. 3, Jan. 1961, pp. 6-8.

Evans, John W. "Sacramento Peak Observatory." *The Astronomical Journal*, Vol. 67, No. 10, Dec. 1962, pp. 781-786.

Laubendorfer, William J.; William J. Whitesell; and Charles M. Ernst. "A Low-Cost Aircraft Inertial Navigation System—the Locating System." *American Institute of Aeronautics and Astronautics*, Conference, Minneapolis, Minn., Aug. 16-18, 1965, pp. 87-95.

Mason, William A.; John H. Hollis; and Lawrence G. Sharpe. "Differential Responses of Chimpanzees to Social Stimulation." *Journal of Comparative and Physiological Psychology*, Vol. 55, No. 6, Dec. 1962, pp. 1105-1110.

Real, Mackey J. "Laser Output Power Versus Environmental Changes." *American Society for Mechanical Engineers*, Symposium, University of New Mexico, Oct. 1964.

Rohles, Frederick H. "A Description of the Unique Air Force Facility and Program at the Holloman Aeromedical Research Laboratory." *Aerospace Medicine*, Vol. 33, July 1962, pp. 826-830.

————. "The Development of an Instrumental Skill in the Chimpanzee." *Journal of the Experimental Analysis of Behavior*, Vol. 4, No. 4, Oct. 1961, pp. 323-325.

————; Richard E. Belleville; and Marvin E. Grunzke. "Measurement of Higher Intellectual Functioning in the Chimpanzee." *Aerospace Medicine*, Vol. 32, Feb. 1961, pp. 121-125.

————, and Marvin E. Grunzke. "A Model for Behavioral Research With Mice in Biosatellites." *Aerospace Medicine*, Vol. 32, Aug. 1961, pp. 751-755.

————, and Herbert H. Reynolds. "A Proposed Approach Toward Determining the Psychophysiological Effects of Prolonged Space Flight." *Aerospace Medicine,* Vol. 34, No. 5, May 1963, pp. 441-442.

von Beckh, Harald J. "Experiments With Animals and Human Subjects Under Sub- and Zero-Gravity Conditions During the Dive and Parabolic Flight." *Journal of Aviation Medicine,* Vol. 25, June 1954, pp. 235-241.

————. "Human Reactions During Flight to Acceleration Preceded by or Followed by Weightlessness." *Aerospace Medicine,* Vol. 30, June 1959, pp. 391-409.

————."The Incidence of Motion Sickness During Exposures to the Weightless State." Symposium, *XIth International Astronautical Congress,* Stockholm, Sweden, Aug. 15-20, 1960, pp. 217,224.

————. "Multi-Directional G-Protection During Experimental Sled Runs." Symposium, *Xth International Astronautical Congress,* London, 1959, pp. 671-682.

————. "Multi-Directional G-Protection in Space Flight and During Escape." *Journal of Aviation Medicine,* Vol. 29, May 1958, pp. 335-342.

Published at the Air Force Missile Development Center, Holloman Air Force Base, N.M.:

Beeding, Eli. L. Jr. *Daisy Track Tests.* Test Report Nr. 6. April-June 1957.

————. *Daisy Track Tests.* Test Report Nr. 7. June-December 1957.

————. *Daisy Track Tests.* Test Report Nr. 8. Feb.-May 1958.

————. *Daisy Decelerator Tests.* May 1958-July 1959.

————. *Daisy Decelerator Tests.* July 1959-April 1960.

————. *Human Deceleration Tests.* AFMDC-TN-60-2. Jan. 1960.

Belleville, Richard E., Frederick H. Rohles Jr., Marvin E. Grunzke, and Fogle C. Clark. *Complex Avoidance Behavior in the Chimpanzee and its Application to the Study of Space Environments.* AFMDC-TR-60-27, Sept. 1960.

————, Frederick H. Rohles Jr., and Marvin E. Grunzke. *Behavior of the Chimpanzee on a Complex Multiple Schedule.* AFMDC-TR-61-27, Aug. 1961.

Bushnell, David. *Administrative History of the Aeromedical Field Laboratory,* 1951-1958.

————. *The Aeromedical Field Laboratory—Mission, Organization, and Track-Test Programs,* 1958-1960.

————. *The Beginnings of Guidance System Testing at the Air Force Missile Development Center,* 1955-1959.

————. *The Beginnings of Research in Space Biology at the Air Force Missile Development Center.* 1946-1952.

————. *Contributions of Balloon Operations to Research and Development at the Air Force Missile Development Center,* 1947-1958.

————. *Development of the Nation's Leading Test-Track Facility,* 1956-1960.

————. *Guidance Testing at the Air Force Missile Development Center,* 1960.

————. *History of Research in Space Biology and Biodynamics at the Air Force Missile Development Center,* 1946-1958.

————. *History of Research in Subgravity and Zero-G at the Air Force Missile Development Center,* 1948-1958.

———— *Major Achievements in Biodynamics: Escape Physiology at the Air Force Missile Development Center,* 1953-1958.

————. *Major Achievements in Space Biology at the Air Force Missile Development Center, 1953-1957.*

————. *Origin and Operation of the First Holloman Track, 1949-1956.*

————. *Research Accomplishments in Biodynamics: Deceleration and Impact at the Air Force Missile Development Center, 1955-1958.*

Etter, Kenneth R. *Geological Considerations for Precision High-Speed Rocket Tracks.* AFMDC-TR- 61-21, June 1961.

Farrer, Donald N., and Marvin E. Grunzke. *Training Techniques for the Continuous Avoidance Task with Chimpanzees.* ARL-TDR-64-7, May 1964.

————, and Herbert H. Reynolds. *Chimpanzee Performance During Exposure to 100% Oxygen at 14.7 PSI.* ARL-TDR-62-8, June 1962.

————; Marvin E. Grunzke; Gregg A. Gilbert; Gary T. Barnhart; and Paul D. Jacobs. *Chimpanzee Performance on a Continuous Avoidance Task During Acceleration at Sustained Low Levels.* ARL-TDR-63-6, March 1963.

Godby, Robert O.; Sherwood B. Browning; David S. Belski; and Ellis R. Taylor. *Anthropometric Measurements of Human Sled Subjects.* ARL-TDR-63-13, April 1963.

Grunzke, Marvin E. *Feeding Devices For Use With Primates in Space Flight.* MDC-TDR-61-35, Dec. 1961.

————. *A Restraint Device for Behavioral Research with the Chimpanzee.* MDC-TDR-61-37, n.d.

————; Frederick H. Rohles Jr.; Richard E. Belleville; and Gordon L. Wilson. *Chimpanzee Performance on a Two-Dimensional Discrete Tracking Task.* ARL-TDR-62-16, July 1962.

Hack, William F. *Hyge Shock Test Faciilty at 6571st Aeromedical Research Laboratory.* ARL-TDR-62-22, Sept. 1962.

Kuhn, Ferdinand F. *On Minimizing the Potential Hazards in High Powered CW Laser Experiments.* WP-MDSGD-65-1, n.d.

Pilot and Task Scientists. *Manhigh III USAF Manned Balloon Flight Into the Stratosphere.* AFMDC-TR-60-16, April 1961.

Reynolds, Herbert H.; Marvin E. Grunzke; and Frederick H. Rohles Jr. *The Effects of Exposure to Simulated Launch and Re-entry Profiles on Chimpanzee Performance.* ARL-TDR-62-1, March 1962.

————; Victor Bogo; and Frederick H. Rohles Jr. *A Multiple Avoidance Schedule for Measuring Temporal Processes in the Chimpanzee.* ARL-TDR-63-8, April 1963.

————; Gregg A. Gilbert; Victor Bogo; and Gary T. Barnhart. *Chimpanzee Performance During Eight Days of Simulated Orbital Flight.* ARL-TDR-64-2, Feb. 1964.

————, and Frederick H. Rohles Jr. *Behavioral Research With Animals in a Manned Space Laboratory.* ARL-TR-64-17, Nov. 1964.

Rohles, Frederick H. Jr. *Behavioral Measurements on Animals Participating in Space Flight.* AFMDC-TN-60-5, March 1960.

————. *A Theory Concerning the Development of an Instrumental Sequence in the Chimpanzee.* AFMDC-TR-61-4, March 1961.

————, and Marvin E. Grunzke. *A Continuous Tracking Device for Primates.* AFMDC-TR-60-10, April 1960.

————, and Herbert H. Reynolds. *A Proposed Approach Toward Determining the Psychological Effects of Prolonged Manned Space Flight.* ARL-TDR-62-28, Dec. 1962.

————; Marvin E. Grunzke; and Herbert H. Reynolds. *A Detailed Account of Chimpanzee Performance During the Ballistic and Orbital Project Mercury Flights.* ARL-TDR-62-15, July 1962.

————; Herbert H. Reynolds; and Marvin E. Grunzke. *A 30-Day Study of Chimpanzee Performance on a Self-paced Task for Food and Water.* ARL-TDR-63-15, May 1963.

————; Herbert H. Reynolds; and Carroll Brown. *Diurnal Temperature Changes in a Chimpanzee During a 14-day Restraint Test.* ARL-TDR-63-2, Jan. 1963.

————; Herbert H. Reynolds; Marvin E. Grunzke; and Donald N. Farrer. *A Laboratory Model For a Fourteen Day Orbital Flight With a Chimpanzee.* AFMDC-TR-61-33, Oct. 1961.

————; George V. Pegram; Herbert H. Reynolds; Marvin E. Grunzke; and Donald N. Farrer. *A Complex Avoidance Schedule For Stress and Drug Research With Primates.* ARL-TDR-63-16, May 1963.

Schock, Grover J. D. *Perception of the Horizontal and Vertical in Simulated Subgravity Conditions.* AFMDC-TN-59-13, June 1959. (ASTIA Document AD 215464.)

————. *A Study of Animal Reflexes During Exposure to Subgravity and Weightlessness.* AFMDC-TN-59-12, June 1959. (ASTIA Document AD 215463).

Stapp, John Paul; Sidney T. Lewis; and James J. Ryan. *Preliminary Investigations of a Hydraulic Bumper and Roll-Over Structure.* AFMDC-TN-58-5, Feb. 1958. (ASTIA Document AD 135007.)

Stingeley, Norman E. *Acceleration-Deceleration Studies of Project Mercury Chimpanzees.* Revised April 1961.

————. *Countdown and Procedures for Project Mercury Atlas-5 Flight (Chimpanzee Subject).* ARL-TDR-62-17, Oct. 1962.

————. *The Physiological Responses of Chimpanzees to Simulated Launch and Re-entry Accelerations.* ARL-TDR-62-11, July 1962.

von Beckh, Harald J. *Flight Experiments About Human Reactions to Accelerations Which Are Followed or Preceded by the Weightless State.* AFMDC-TN-58-15, Dec. 1958. (ASTIA Document 154108.)

————. *Physiology of Launching and Re-entry Stress in Rodents.* AFMDC-TN-58-11, Aug. 1958. (ASTIA Document 154105.).

————, and Grover J. D. Schock. *Centrifuge Experiments on High-G Loads in Mice and Their Possible Alleviation by Multidirectional Anti-G Devices.* AFMDC-TN- 58-10, Aug. 1958. (ASTIA Document 154104.)

Ward, William E. *Altered Environments for Biological Specimens. 1. Restraint Conditioning of Large Biological Specimens.* AFMDC-TN-59-36, Oct. 1959.

Winzen Research Inc. *Manhigh I.* AFMDC-TR-59-24, June 1959. (ASTIA Document AD 215867.)

Wright, Harold V. *Central Inertial Guidance Test Facility Guide, Volume I, Facilities and Capabilities.* MDC-TDR-62-4, March 1962.

UNAUTHORED TECHNICAL REPORTS PUBLISHED AT THE AIR FORCE MISSILE DEVLOPMENT CENTER:

Holloman Track Capabilities. Track Test Division. AFMDC-TR-60-24, Nov. 1960.

Holloman Track Capabilities. Deputy for Guidance Test. MDC-TDR-62-9, Sept. 1962.

The Holloman Track, Facilities and Capabilities. MDC-TD-65-2, June 1965.

Special High Altitude Chamber Facility (Stratosphere Chamber) for Upper Atmosphere Research and Combined Environmental Testing. April 1959.

INDEX